DIVISION OF LABOR
IN CELLS

DIVISION OF LABOR IN CELLS

GEOFFREY H. BOURNE

DEPARTMENT OF ANATOMY, EMORY UNIVERSITY, ATLANTA, GEORGIA

ACADEMIC PRESS • NEW YORK AND LONDON

ACADEMIC PRESS INC.
111 FIFTH AVENUE, NEW YORK 3, NEW YORK

United Kingdom Edition published by
ACADEMIC PRESS INC. (LONDON) LTD.
BERKELEY SQUARE HOUSE, LONDON W.1

Library of Congress Catalog Card Number 61–18300

PRINTED IN THE UNITED STATES OF AMERICA

Preface

is a study that provides intriguing problems for both experimental and theoretical scientists. During the last few years new cytological techniques have been developed which have fundamentally altered our approach to research in the field.

Through use of these techniques considerable light has been shed upon the complexities of cell structure and function, but so much remains to be learned that in some instances discoveries serve chiefly to open up new vistas for research and to point out still more challenging unresolved problems.

This volume is concerned with the relationships between structure and the chemical and biochemical composition of cells in general and of several specialized types of cells. It has been planned as a brief synthesis of certain aspects of modern cell biology that will provide some biochemical background for graduate students in biology and anatomy and a morphological basis for graduate students in biochemistry. It is hoped that it will find a niche in the libraries not only of general biologists but also of pathologists and others who are interested in cell biology.

Division of labor is evidenced by the way in which the various parts of the cell perform important but different functions according to the task for which each is structurally and chemically suited. For example, the nucleolus synthe-

v

sizes a considerable amount of protein and ribonucleic acid; oxidative activities occur in the mitochondria with the consequent production of ATP which plays its vital role in glandular, muscle, nerve, and other cells. A striking factor is the degree to which all parts of the cell cooperate to build up an ordered and controlled metabolic picture. Among the promising areas for further investigations are the mechanism of control of the endocrine system over the cell, the relationship of vitamins and other nutritive factors to the physiology of the cell, and the role of the cytoplasmic (endoplasmic) reticulum.

The author was encouraged to prepare this small book because of the many requests which he received for reprints of a paper on "Division of Labor in Cells" which he presented at a conference on the Chemical Organization of Cells sponsored in August, 1958 by the Pathology Study Section of the National Institutes of Health and later published in the *Journal of Laboratory Investigation.*

The subject of cell biology is one that is advancing with considerable speed and there have been significant advances since the book was written, the reader will therefore not find references to "messenger RNA" as such, its function and significance are referred to but not under that name.

The work referred to in the text which was carried out in the author's laboratory was performed with the aid of the following grants: Muscular Dystrophy Associations of America Inc., No. B-1914 and No. B-2038 from the National Institute of Neurological Diseases and Blindness, No. A-3090 and No. A-2050 from the National Institute of Arthritis and Metabolic Diseases.

The author is greatly indebted to Dr. Henry Hoberman, Dr. Keith Porter, and Dr. Maurice Sandler for reading the manuscript and for many helpful comments.

GEOFFREY H. BOURNE

Emory University
Atlanta 22, Georgia
May 9, 1962

Contents

CHAPTER I

Introduction

FAR AWAY IN THE DISTANT past, when the primeval seas bubbled and steamed, when ultraviolet light of great intensity streamed onto the surface of the earth, molecules of polypeptides, of long-chain fatty acids, steroids of various sorts, and purines and pyrimidines ultimately to form part of the nucleic acids, went through the seething pangs of synthesis. Both purines and pyrimidines have recently been found in the interior of meteorites —thus they are not unique to this world and indicate that nucleic acid synthesis may be occurring elsewhere in space.

These compounds, floating free in a warm soup, performed no organized activity. They reacted indiscriminately with each other, blindly, with no form or purpose. Then, groups of molecules responding to electrical and surface-forming forces became orientated in a way which produced a membrane.

Presumably these membranes which were forming on the surface of the water were at first simply flat structures, but "one day" through inter-reaction of the various molecules a membrane formed a little vesicle. Many other vesicles became formed, and here we had for the first time the potentialities for the development of living structures, for the membrane cut off the contents of the bag from the environment. What could have been the composition of such membranes? Perhaps the amino acids were formed into proteins at the time that this happened. Proteins, in general, have a remarkable property of spreading in a very thin film upon the surface of water—even when they are themselves in solution they are capable of forming these thin films. Compounds such as steroids and fats, i.e., compounds which have a preponderance of hydrocarbon groupings which makes them only slightly soluble in water, also have the ability to spread on surfaces and to have a particular orientation so that their polar groups will, in general, be in contact with water or with other polar groups, and those parts which have hydrocarbon groups will be out of contact with the water. Furthermore, lipoprotein films which combine both these two types of compounds, can even be formed artificially, for instance cholesterol and the protein gliadin have been used to produce such a film. These films have considerable elasticity and a good deal of strength.

Within the little vesicles we have mentioned, the reorganization of the molecules went on, and eventually a vesicle formed within the parent vesicle which formed a structure similar to the nucleus. Combinations between proteins and nucleic acids formed a basis for inheritance of some of the characters of the cell in a way which we do not yet understand fully. By a slow and gradual process of evolution a complicated structure we now know to be a cell was built up and from it developed the multicellular organisms, animal and plant. At the stage when the multicellular organisms were evolving, it is not even certain that the cell was completely developed in the way we know it at the moment, it probably had a much simpler character than present day cells.

The bags or vesicles contained proteins, fats, phospholipids, carbohydrates, minerals, enzymes, vitamins, and water. Now if one normally shook such components up in a little bag not much would happen, although no doubt there would be some linkup of some of the molecules to form structures. For example, if collagen is disaggregated with citrate and then is left to stand after the citrate had been removed, many of these groups of molecules reform into collagen units or even collagen fibers. Something of this sort could occur in the type of vesicle we have described if the right molecules got together. On the other hand, in the beginning very little activity characteristic of the living cell would develop. In the presence of their substrates, for instance, many of the enzymes present would have some action, but for some of the enzymes the pH would be wrong and in such a mixture there would probably be only one uniform pH and the temperature would not be optimal. There would be no mechanism for removal of reaction products from the site of their formation, and the reactions would be rapidly saturated with them and would grind to a stop.

The secret of the complex activity of the living cell lies in the isolation or partial isolation or even the timed isolation of its various activities. This is achieved by the presence of various membranes. The nuclear membrane guards the activity of the nucleus, and the Golgi apparatus and the mitochondria have membranes which permit them to carry out activities in partial but not complete seclusion. Fig. 1 shows the structure of typical cells, the lower illustration shows a single cell under the high power of the microscope. Fig. 2 demonstrates in diagram form the elements of the cell as seen under the electron microscope.

It is of interest that natural, fresh water frequently contains films and these are probably derived, according to Goldacre, from decomposed biological material. They appear to contain protein or lipoprotein and in many ways possibly resemble the type of film just described from which cells were probably originally formed. It is of further interest that films such as these, upon collapsing, can spontaneously form vesicles or cylinders, e.g., the wind may cause a collapse of the film. In the case of water passing under a floating barrier, for example, when a stream disappears underground, the surface film is carried toward the point of entry, and according to Goldacre, may be concen-

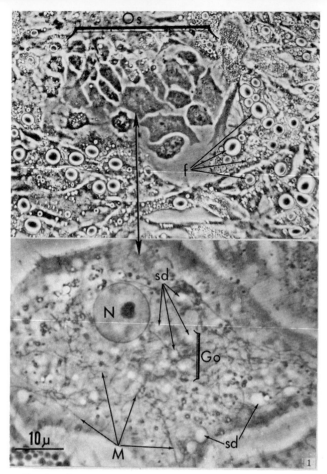

FIG. 1. *The living cells under the optical microscope.*
Migrating cells from two week old embryo chick leg bones
after three weeks of cultivation under strips of cellophane.
The top illustration shows a nest of osteoblasts (Os) sur-
rounded by a dense stroma of large fat droplet (f) con-
taining fibroblasts. The lower photograph shows one
osteoblast under high power magnification. Specific parts
of this cell are the nucleus (N), the Golgi complex (Go),
secretory droplets (sd) emanating from the Golgi complex,
and long filamentous mitochondria (M). (Preparation and
photography by George G. Rose.)

FIG. 2 *(right). What the electron microscope shows. The*
fine structure of the Golgi complex, the nucleolus, the
basophilic substance, and the mitochondria are shown
diagrammatically. (From "General Cytology," De Robertis,
Nowinski and Saez, 1960, W. B. Saunders.)

trated. Compression of this film causes a wrinkling and if the wrinkles become sufficiently pinched the walls finally touch underneath the wrinkles and complete cylinders may be detached which separate from the rest of the film. These cylinders themselves can form vesicles which would resemble the primeval vesicles previously mentioned; some may contain air and some the underlying water. Sometimes instead of cylinders, fibers may be produced. It is of interest that the properties of these collapsed lipoprotein films (which can actually be produced in the laboratory) have, according to Goldacre, many similarities to those of the membranes of living cells.

Proteins and other macromolecules, according to Brownell, seem to be able to form in nature without any special difficulty. Presumably small organic molecules could form quite easily under the circumstances in which the earth existed at one time. Carbon monoxide, carbon dioxide, hydrogen, nitrogen, and other gases including some inorganic catalysts such as various metals and ions can produce small organic chemicals which, once formed may go through a process of polymerization to build up larger and more complex molecules. This, in fact, has been done in the laboratory. It is very likely that amino acids and proteins existed in the soupy seas of the earth for a long time, perhaps before membranes formed; on the other hand, it is possible that as the former substances were produced many of them became or-

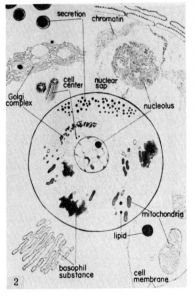

2

ganized into surface films which became membranes and subsequently divided up into vesicles. As mentioned earlier, artificial membranes can easily be formed, and mixtures of fatty substances, alkalis, proteins, and inorganic salts are very suitable for this purpose. Hereira has even formed in this way, what he describes as artificial amoebae which were persuaded to produce types of amoeboid movement. But, as Goldacre points out, such movements are uncontrolled, and what is so important in cells is the fact that there is a very considerable degree of control by the cell over itself. Nevertheless the studies of Hereira help us perhaps to understand how objects comparable to cells, in other words, isolated vesicles containing macromolecules could have been produced in the first place.

Goldacre himself points out that the essential step in the evolution of the cell was the formation around a chemical system of what he describes as a relatively impermeable envelope in the beginning. But, as he also points out, what was presumably a relatively simple structure at first must have undergone a considerable amount of further development, and membranes of present day cells are relatively complicated structures which take quite an active part in regulating the compounds and ions that go in and out of the cell. For this purpose they seem to have absorbed, adsorbed, or incorporated enzymes in some way onto or into their surfaces, and these enzymes play a part in the process of active transport. Goldacre's concluding comment, however, was that "it appears that the cell uses and may be found in the future to be using mechanisms that are not very different from processes which are already available in the surface films of nature."

CHAPTER II

The structure
of the cell membrane

THE INTRODUCTORY CHAP-
ter has suggested that both protein and lipoid substances*
may be concerned in the structure of cell membranes.
Let us trace briefly the origin of our present knowledge
of the structure of cell membranes. Overton in 1895, was
originally responsible for the idea that lipids were important in cell membrane structure. He made this suggestion
because of the relative ease with which lipid soluble substances penetrated the cells. At that time there was no clear
idea as to what types of lipid molecules were present or as
to how they were arranged. In 1917, Langmuir and other
workers made deductions about the arrangement of molecules in molecular films spread on water surfaces, and these
have been described as being of fundamental importance to
the modern concepts of the cell membrane structure. Langmuir suggested (as mentioned in the introduction) that
lipids at an interface of air and water arrange themselves
in a monolayer with the polar ends of the molecules directed
toward the water interface and the nonpolar ends at the air
interface. In 1925, Gorter and Grendell found that the
total amount of lipid they could extract from a red cell

* Lipoid is a generic term used to include ether and alcohol soluble
compounds such as phospholipids, fats, fatty acids, cholesterol, and
other steroids.

ghost† when spread in a monolayer occupied about twice the area of the membranes of the red cells. They suggested, therefore, that the lipid was arranged in the membrane as a bimolecular leaflet in which the hydrophilic polar groups were at the inner and outer surfaces and the hydrophobic carbon chains were directed toward each other in the interior of the membrane. This was a simple and attractive model. It is difficult to imagine however how such a simple structure could account for all the various functions of the cell membrane.

Dr. G. D. Robertson has described the next stages of the development of our knowledge of the cell membrane. Briefly these are as follows: Harvey and Shapiro in the 1930's and also Cole during the same period studied the surface tension of starfish eggs and came to the conclusion that, at the ranges of pH's which apparently occurred inside cells, most pure lipoid substances gave surface tension values of the order of 5 dynes/cm.^{2} or more. But intracellular oil drops were found to have a surface tension of only 0.2 dyne/cm.^{2} The surface tension of whole starfish eggs as estimated by the force required to compress them, is even lower than this. Thus, if only a purely lipid/water interface is concerned, these low values for the living cell cannot be explained. Danielli and Harvey demonstrated that there was some substance on the cell membrane which was responsible for such low values. This substance was a surface active agent of a cytoplasmic nature and appeared to be protein. Apparently in natural membranes all lipid polar substances were covered with at least a monolayer of protein. Danielli and Davson eventually proposed that cell membranes in general had the same sort of structure and that this consisted of one or more bimolecular leaflets of lipid with each polar surface having on it a monolayer of protein. (See Fig. 3.)

---

† A red cell ghost is obtained when red cells are hemolyzed and so lose their contents, and the empty membranes (the ghosts) are centrifuged out of solution and analyzed.

In 1936, Schmitt, using polarization microscopy, concluded that at least in red cell membranes the lipid molecules which were present had their carbon chains radially oriented. Thus we can picture the cell membrane as being composed of two layers of lipid molecules radially arranged (at right angles to the surface of the membrane) and a monolayer of protein applied to both the inner and outer surfaces of the membrane, with the long axes of the molecules lying parallel to the surface.

It had been suggested in the past that the cell membrane contained either pure lipid or pure protein, with pores of dimensions about the size of a large molecule, or that it was in the form of a mosaic containing either pure lipid or pure protein in various areas. However, this seems unlikely now except in some special cases. It is of interest that a common structure for the cell membrane exists in cells as diverse as erythrocytes, axons of nerve cells, muscle fibers, leucocytes of the blood, yeast cells, algal cells, the cells of higher plants, and the ova of echinoderms, e.g., sea urchins and starfish. It seems very likely, however, that there are variations to some extent between the membranes of the various cells; nevertheless it is highly probable that a general structural pattern does exist for all of them. A typical example of

FIG. 3. *The structure of the cell membrane. This photograph illustrates the pauci-molecular theory of Davson and Danielli. The center layer is lipid. The peripheral lipid molecules on both sides are oriented at right angles to the surface, superimposed on them is a monolayer of protein (spheres). (From "The Permeability of Natural Membranes" Davson and Danielli, 1943, Cambridge Univ. Press.)*

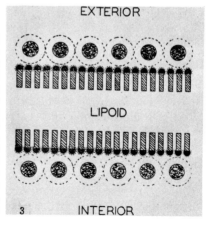

EXTERIOR

LIPOID

INTERIOR

variation was demonstrated by Mudd and Mudd who showed that erythrocytes are preferentially wetted by oil, and leucocytes by water; this indicates that molecules at the surface of the membranes differ.

Studies with the electron-microscope (see Figs. 4 and 5) have demonstrated that those membranes which have been studied have a thickness of the order of about 80 A (10,000 A $= 1\mu$) so that they are about $1/25\mu$ thick. Dr. Keith Porter has pointed out that the first electron-microscope photographs demonstrated the cell membrane as a solid structure, but that, as the technique improved and better resolution was obtained, the membrane was seen to be composed of two thin, very dense lines with a space between them. The lines measured about 25 A each and the space between them measured about 30 A across. It is tempting to suggest that the two outer lines represent the protein parts of the membrane, and the central space the phospholipid portion, but this has yet to be proven. This electron-microscope pattern of structure and size is general in cell membranes—it is present, for example, in the nuclear membrane, the membranes of the endoplasmic reticulum, and those of the mitochondria.

In due course no doubt the electron-microscope will shed further light on the nature of the membranes and possibly the differences between the many types of membranes in various cells, but there are limitations to what it can do at the present moment.

Some of the ideas of the nature of the cell membrane have been derived from a study of its fundamental properties. First of all it is known that lipid-soluble substances have a preferential permeability across cell membranes, and this suggests that there must be in the membrane a continuous layer which is composed of phosphatides, steroids or fats or combinations of those substances. Also cell membranes have a high electrical resistance which, Danielli points out, is further evidence that there must be a continuous layer of lipids. Another property is the existence of a low surface tension at the surface of the cell membranes.

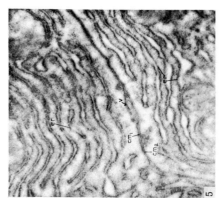

FIG. 5. The cell membranes at the junction of two acinar pancreatic cells (cm_1 and cm_2) are shown and the endoplasmic reticulum (er) can also be seen in both cells. (From Palade and Siekevitz, J. Biophys. Biochem. Cytol., 1956, 2, 671.)

FIG. 4 (left). The cell membrane as demonstrated in the electron microscope. It can be seen to be composed of a central light line surrounded by two dark (osmiophilic lines). The edge of the nucleus can be seen on the lower left. (Preparation and photograph by Dr. Keith Porter.)

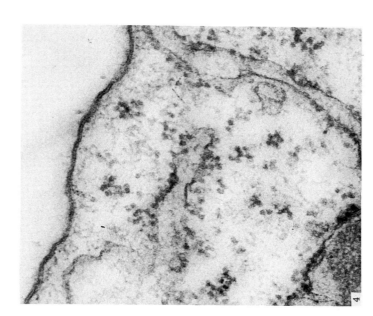

We have mentioned earlier how Danielli has suggested that this property indicates that on the surfaces of the membrane protein layers are adsorbed. Cell membranes are disrupted by digitonin which has a special ability to form a complex with cholesterol, and this suggests that this latter compound may play a part in the structure of the membrane.

Analysis of red cell ghosts has in fact demonstrated that a relatively large amount of cholesterol is present in the membrane. An interesting theory concerning the structure of the red cell membrane was proposed by Winkler and Bungenburg de Jong in 1941. This theory gives the free cholesterol the role of stabilizer for the charged phospholipid molecules thus enabling them to give form to the membrane. The essential features of this structure are seen in Fig. 6. This concept has been elaborated by Frey-Wyssling in 1953, whose studies on submicroscopic morphology and its relation to the chemical constituents of the cell are of fundamental importance. It is of interest to notice that in the two issues where cholesterol has been assigned the major role of structural component, it is present mainly if not entirely in the free unesterified form. There is one striking difference however in the nature of the cholesterol in the myelin sheath and the red cell. In the myelin sheath it is apparently stable and once deposited

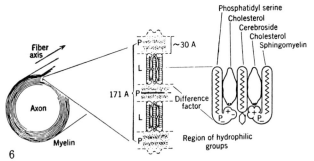

Fig. 6. *Molecular structure of the myelin sheath as suggested by Schmitt, Bear and Palmer. (From J. Cell & Comp. Physiol., 1941, 18, 31.)*

under normal conditions remains static for life. In the red blood cell there is a steady turnover and exchange with plasma cholesterol. In general, in tissues where there is active metabolism of cholesterol, esterified cholesterol is found, the amount varying from tissue to tissue.

One should, perhaps, at this point say a word about the composition of the myelin sheath since this is in a sense an extended membrane (see Fig. 6). (A more detailed description of the myelin sheath is given at the end of this book.) Finean (1953, 1956), from his studies on the x-ray diffraction pattern of myelin, suggested that it was probably composed of alternate layers of lipid and nonlipid, the nonlipid probably being protein. The lipid molecules appear to be curled or tilted so that their full length is not extended, and there is probably a stable complex formed between the cholesterol molecule and the larger phospholipid molecules. It is postulated that the free hydroxyl group of the cholesterol is important in binding the molecule by associating with the polar end of the lipid chain which it curls round. The hydrocarbon part of the cholesterol molecule is bound to the phospholipid by Van der Waal's forces. Cholesterol has a high dielectric constant and because of this it might act as an insulating agent.

THE PERMEABILITY OF CELL MEMBRANES

Danielli has discussed on several occasions the various problems associated with the permeability of natural membranes, and the account which follows is taken largely from his writings.

Penetration of compounds

Danielli points out that there are three sites of resistance to free diffusion in cell membranes: (1) the membrane/water interface for diffusion into the membrane; (2) the membrane/water interface for diffusion from the membrane into the water; and (3) the interior of the membrane. Every molecule which requires to pass into the interior of the cell has to get through these three sites of resistance. A molecule which has polar groups (–OH groups), as opposed, for instance, to nonpolar groups such as methylene, forms at least one hydrogen bond with water for each polar group; all these hydrogen bonds must be fractured simultaneously if the molecule is to penetrate even into the lipoid membrane. Glycerol, having three OH groups, must acquire sufficient kinetic energy to break three hydrogen bonds simultaneously before it can penetrate into the membrane. This involves a large amount of energy, consequently resistance 1 (diffusion from water to membrane) is so high for glycerol that resistances 2 and 3 are reduced to insignificance. On the other hand, a molecule such as methyl alcohol which has only one OH group and one CH_3 group penetrates easily into the membrane and can also pass easily out of the lipoid layer into water, and presumably ethyl alcohol (C_2H_5OH) can function similarly. Thus we find that for such molecules the rate of diffusion across the interfaces is very large compared with rate of diffusion across the membrane. The interior of the membrane in the case of these compounds is the most important factor controlling penetration. Differing from these examples are molecules which are predominantly hydrocarbon in nature such as carotene ($C_{40}H_{56}$). With a molecule such as this, resistance 1 is insignificant; the molecule has no polar groups and thus even resistance 3 is not enormous; however, resistance 2 is very large indeed, because the hydrocarbon groups are hydrophobic and a considerable amount of kinetic energy is required to transfer CH_2 groups from lipid into water. When many such groups are present they must all be transferred simultaneously from the lipoid layer into water, since otherwise the molecule remains substantially part of the lipoid layer and cannot diffuse away into the aqueous phase.

With these examples in mind, Danielli classified penetrating molecules into four groups.

(A) Molecules with few polar and few nonpolar groups

—for these resistance 3 is most important and they can penetrate comparatively rapidly e.g., oxygen and methyl alcohol.

(B) Molecules having a predominantly polar character—for these resistance 1 is most important and penetration is slow, included are glycerols, sugar, and glycogen.

(C) Molecules having few polar and many nonpolar groups—resistance 2 is most important, penetration is slow e.g., carotene, vitamin A, and fat.

(D) Molecules having many polar and many nonpolar groups—resistances 1 and 2 are both important and penetration is slow e.g., polyhydroxylic bile acids, the glucuronide of oestrin, and proteins.

Danielli has pointed out that these principles of membrane permeability have a distinct physiological significance. For instance, oxygen is required in large amounts by the cell and carbon dioxide must be disposed of rapidly, and both of these substances can penetrate the cell membrane rapidly. On the other hand, the first products of glucose utilization, for example, by muscle cells are glycerol derivatives, these are valuable and the cell membrane does not let them get through too easily and so they escape only slowly. During sustained work lactic acid is formed—this would be toxic if it accumulated. The cell membrane is relatively permeable to lactic acid which thus can escape into the blood, and this permits violent exercise to be maintained for a much longer period than would be the case if the cell membrane was impermeable to lactic acid. Amino acids penetrate all membranes moderately well but protein penetrates badly and, therefore, amino acids are stored as protein. Fatty acids will penetrate moderately well, but neutral fat very poorly, therefore fatty acids are stored as neutral fat. Glucose which can get in and out of cells fairly rapidly is polymerized in liver cells to form glycogen which passes the cell membrane only with great difficulty. Each of these three latter products, to which the membranes are impermeable, are the results of polymerization of simpler compounds.

It is of interest that, when compounds which are diffusing through a cell membrane from outside to inside are being incorporated into some compound within the cell, they appear to penetrate the membrane more easily. A typical example of this can be drawn from amino acids. If they are being actively incorporated into proteins, the rate of diffusion through the membrane will be much more rapid than if they were not being incorporated. Presumably, if they are being built into proteins, they cease to accumulate and so cease to build up a concentration gradient against the passage of further amino acids.

Detoxification mechanisms also take advantage of the principles of the cell membrane permeability. For instance, toxic substances which might penetrate the cell membrane become conjugated with amino acids, sulfuric acid, or glucuronic acid. Thus toxic cell-penetrating substances such as bromobenzene or menthol are converted into new molecules which penetrate the cells with great difficulty and once in the bloodstream tend to be filtered off by the glomeruli of the kidneys and cannot be reabsorbed from the urine and returned to the bloodstream by the kidney tubules.

Penetration of ions through cell membranes

Penetration of ions through cell membranes is of special interest because for instance, Na^+ ions are more concentrated outside the cell (in the body fluids) and K^+ ions are more concentrated inside the cell, yet we know that K ions will pass into the cell and Na ions will pass out. Both these passages thus take place against a concentration gradient, and this can only occur by the application of energy. It is claimed that oxidative enzymes and phosphatases play a part in the movement of ions in and out of membranes; a process which is known as "active transport." Substances which interfere with the activity of these enzymes have been shown in many cases to interfere with the movement in or out of the cell of both sodium and potassium. There are certain specialized cell membranes, e.g., the cell membrane of the intestinal cells, in which the distal edge of the cell is folded to produce a larger number of extremely small fingerlike processes called microvilli; these microvilli are covered with a typical cell membrane. There are a large number of dephosphorylating enzymes localized around these microvilli. Their precise function in this position is not known, but it is almost certain, however, that they play a part in active transport by utilizing the energy derived from the hydrolysis of high-energy phosphates.

It is obvious from what we have said, therefore, that the cell membrane, in general, is a very selective structure and exercises a good deal of control over the cell by deciding what goes in or out and by enabling the cell to be isolated from its environment. In this way it permits labor to go on in the cell which may be quite different from that going on in a neighboring cell, or in the body fluids surrounding the cell. Here then is the first division of labor in the cell to be described by us.

However the story is not yet ended. In 1952–54, Danielli proposed the structure of the cell membrane which explained the way in which large protein molecules in the cell membrane could permit the passage of ions through the membrane. Danielli conceived of a long protein molecule extending right through the membrane and passing outside it. This end became attached to an ion and then by contraction pulled the latter through into the interior of the membrane. (See Fig. 7.)

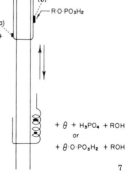

FIG. 7. *Diagram of Danielli's theory of secretion by a contractile protein. (From Soc. Exp. Biol., Symposia, 1952, 6, 1.)*

According to Lundgard and Hodgkin, a cytochrome oxidase energy-producing system is involved in the penetration of ions. They claim that their ion moving system requires adenosine triphosphatase (ATPase), creatine phosphatase, and cytochrome oxidase. Conway has produced a redox-pump hypothesis that attempts to explain the penetration of ions through cell membranes by a mechanism which involves the successive oxidation and reduction of a compound in the membranes; possibly a phospholipid provides the energy for the movement of ions in this way. Phosphatidic acid is now thought to be concerned with ion movements through membranes

The possible relationship of phosphatases to cell membrane permeability has also been mentioned in connection with the microvilli (brush borders) of intestinal epithelium. The passage of glucose across the mebranes of gut cells could be explained by a mechanism involving these enzymes. It is of interest that in yeast cells too there is some evidence that phosphatases are localized on the membrane and that these enzymes are also involved in the permeability not only to glucose but also to phosphates. Phosphatases are also present on the brush borders of the kidney tubule cells where a good deal of absorption takes place. More recent work has indicated that ribonuclease may play a part in the penetration of cell membranes by ions. Lansing and Rosenthal and Tenardo, for instance, showed that when ribonuclease was added from the outside to certain cells, it modified their permeability to ions; Brachet and Leduc found exactly the same thing for amphibian eggs. According to Brachet "amphibian eggs swell very much when they are immersed in a ribonuclease solution and since cell membranes often give strong cytochemical tests for ribonucleic acid it might well be that the integrity of this nucleic acid is of importance for normal permeability."

In a more recent paper (1954), Danielli made a suggestion that the cell membrane consisted, as suggested before, of bimolecular leaflets of lipoid with protein molecules stretched both inside and outside the membrane, but that it also contains a series of pores which he calls polar pores (see Fig. 8). In other words, groups of protein molecules are oriented radially with their polar groups directed toward the interior of the pore and such molecules are thus able to control the penetration of the compounds or substances through this pore according to their polar group affinities.

In a recent paper, Danielli (1959) discusses the association with all membranes of a group of enzymes, which are called "permeases." These compounds he says "permit either facilitated diffusion or active transfer of 'signal' molecules across the membranes." It is possible that insulin may function as a permease for cells of certain organs. To quote Danielli again "Once permease becomes incorporated in the plasma membrane the situation is transformed: specific substrates can penetrate, more permease will become available by induced synthesis, induced enzyme will appear, and a whole range of further induced enzymes may appear in re-

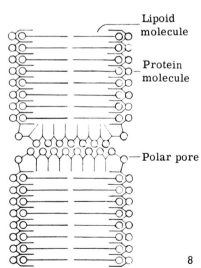

Lipoid molecule

Protein molecule

Polar pore

FIG. 8. *Diagram of cell membrane as suggested by Danielli in 1954. (From Colston papers, 7, 1, 1954.)*

8

sponse to the action of the induced enzymes of the inducing substrate. Thus a transient infection with permease may potentially change drastically the state of differentiation of a cell—possibly even result in carcinogenesis." It is very likely that there will be considerable further developments in this subject of permeases and their relation to cell membrane permeability and these will be awaited with interest.

A further development which should be noted when considering problems of penetration of compounds into cells is that of pinocytosis. This literally means "drinking by cells" and was first described by Warren Lewis many years ago in tissue culture cells. In this process, these cells were seen by a pseudopodial-like movement to engulf a droplet of culture fluid in which they were lying. The process was equivalent and similar to the phagocytosis of solid food by the *Amoeba,* only in the case of the tissue

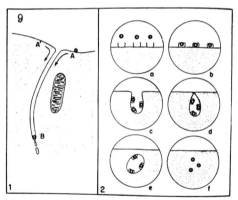

Fig. 9. *Diagrammatic representation of pinocytosis after Bennett (1956, J. Biophys. Biochem. Cytol., 2, part 2, Suppl. 99). Pinocytosis is described by Holter (Int. Rev. Cytol., 1959, 8, 481) as "a mechanism for the discontinuous uptake of solutions by invagination and vesiculation of the cell surface. The quantities taken up at a single gulp cover a wide range from submicroscopic vesicles to large vesicles and there is no sharp demarcation between phagocytosis on one side and molecular permeation on the other." This is illustrated in the diagram.*

culture cell it is a droplet of fluid that is engulfed. Now it seems that the cells of multicellular animals even *in vivo* can do the same sort of thing though there may be specialized parts of the cell membrane which carry out the process (see Fig. 9). A case in point is the kidney tubule cell. From the basal part of the cell, long internal extensions of the cell membrane pass a considerable distance up into the interior of the cytoplasm. They are present in some other cells too and are called "caveolae intracellulares." The cell appears to be able to imbibe droplets of fluid by an engulfing movement of the membranes of these caveolae. It is possible too that the cell membranes of a variety of cells may be able to carry out pinocytosis even without the presence of these intracellular membranous extensions. (See Figs. 10 and 11, page 23.)

Thus we see that, if a cell really "wants" to take in a few macromolecules that pass its membranes with difficulty, it can always take them by "the scruff of the neck" and pull them pinocytotically into its interior.

DIFFERENTIAL CENTRIFUGATION

One of the developments in technique which has done an enormous amount to advance our studies of the cell is that of differential centrifugation, and an account of this technique should be given before we pass on to the study of the cell components.

The extraction of cell components from tissues dates back a very long time, and studies on the chemical nature of the nuclei were carried out during the 19th century on nuclei obtained from pus cells by differential centrifugation. More recently, tissues have been homogenized and spun down at different speeds, and the different portions of the cell separate out according to their density. For example, if a homogenate is taken up in $0.8\text{-}M$ sucrose solution which tends to preserve the morphological character of most cell structures and it is then spun at about 1000 r.p.m., the cell debris and the nuclei come down. The nuclei can be differentially centrifuged again from the cell debris so that a pure nuclear fraction suitable for chemical analysis can be obtained. At a higher speed, the mitochondria and at still higher speeds, the particles of glycogen, one part of the microsomes, and other parts which are really fragmented endoplasmic reticulum aggregate at the bottom of the centrifuge tube. As a result of this technique, studies of the enzyme content of the nuclei and mitochondria have been made in great detail. This has caused some controversy because of the possibility that soluble enzymes and other substances might be leached from the nuclei during the homogenization procedures. Dilute acids, e.g., citric and acetic acids, have been used as homogenization fluids and possess certain advantages in that they make the tissue fragile and thus more easily broken. They also appear to harden the nuclear membrane and help to preserve the nuclei intact. However, they are unsuitable for enzymatic studies, and tissue homogenized in solutions of sucrose are usually used for this purpose. The latter method is claimed, because of the low ionic strength of the sucrose solution, to reduce greatly the loss of materials from the nuclei. It is said, in fact, that proteins and nucleic acids do not get through the membranes but low molecular weight substances do suffer some loss by this method. Allfrey and his colleagues at the Rockefeller Institute have tried to reduce any type of loss from the nucleus by freeze-drying the tissue and then grinding and floating it in nonaqueous media. Although in many respects this is advantageous, it appears difficult to be certain that small fragments of cytoplasm

Fig. 10. *Phase contrast study of pinocytosis in* Amoeba proteus. *Channels (white) can be seen extending in from the edge of the cell. (Photograph by David M. Prescott. From Holter, Int. Rev. Cytol., 8, 481, 1959.)*

Fig. 11. *Phase contrast study of pinocytosis in* Amoeba proteus. *Strings of vacuoles can be seen occupying approximately the same position as the channels in Fig. 10. (Photography by David M. Prescott. From Holter, Int. Rev. Cytol., 8, 481, 1959.)*

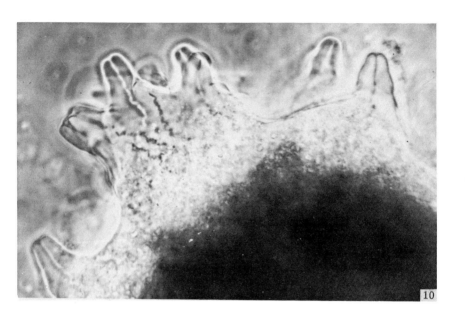

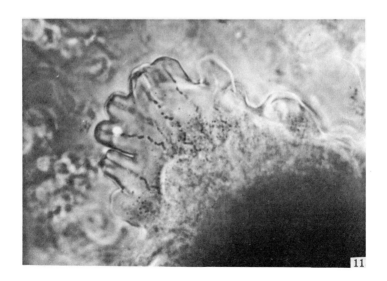

do not stick to the nuclei and contaminate the material. Extremely interesting results have been obtained by this particular technique.

Another check which was made on this differential centrifugation technique was to add various pure enzymes to the homogenate and then to calculate how much was adsorbed on the nuclei, mitochondria, microsomes, and so on and how much was left in the supernatant. Although the amounts taken up with the supernatant varied with different tissues, generally speaking, the results were encouraging enough to indicate that the adsorption of enzymes from the normal supernatant was not really a significant cause of error in this technique.

Roodyn in a recently published review of the enzymic content of isolated nuclei has discussed the possibilities of contamination. He points out that we know that there is a very intimate connection between the endoplasmic reticulum and the nuclear membrane and that it is believed that the nuclear membrane is really a fold of the endoplasmic reticulum. Thus the nuclear fraction could easily be contaminated with this part of the cell. Also there is a possibility that some of the sedimented material may contain whole cells which have escaped homogenization as well as nuclei, and this would be another source of error. There is a possibility too that mitochondria may stick to the isolated nuclei and so also be contaminants. Although a certain amount of contamination is thus possible, it is only significant where a small percentage of total enzyme content of the cell is attributed to the nucleus, in this case it may be due to contamination, but where the nucleus contains an appreciable proportion of the total enzyme activity of the cell then the contamination becomes not very significant.

CHAPTER III

The cytoplasm

WITHIN THE CELL MEM-
brane and separated from the outside (extracellular) world
by it, is the cytoplasm. Does it perform any labor? What is
its contribution to the life and welfare of the cell? First of
all let us find out what we can about its nature.

Cytoplasm chemically is composed of proteins, lipoids
(which include fatty, phospholipid, and steroidal compounds), carbohydrates, mineral salts, and, of course, a
good deal of water (40–80%). The constituents of the protoplasm of animals and plants are generally similar, although
the relative proportions of the various components varies a
good deal in different organisms and probably even in the
same organism under different physiological conditions.
Originally, according to Wilson in his classic work "The
Cell" (1928), the similarity between the protoplasm of
plants and animals was stressed and particularly the importance of protein as a structural element in both of them
(this, of course, can still be accepted). However, the chemical
evidence has since shown that some of the other elements
differ in animals and plants, for instance, the plant protoplasm has rather more carbohydrate in it, and proteins and
lipids are the main constituents of the animal protoplasm.
Protoplasm, in general, behaves and appears to be something
in the nature of a colloidal system which is very complex

and behaves almost always as if it were a viscous liquid. This is particularly well demonstrated by living protoplasm undergoing streaming movements so well demonstrated in plant cells and in animal cells, such as *Amoeba,* when pseudopodia are being produced. Cells which are lying free tend to round up and become spherical when they are resting, and if small fragments of protoplasm are chopped off from cells by a process described technically as "micrurgy," which simply means microsurgery, the little pieces so removed become spherical. Both these facts are in keeping with the conception that protoplasm is a viscous fluid.

Viscosity varies a great deal in different kinds of cells and it varies in the same cell from time to time according to the physiological state of the cell. Sometimes it may set into a semi-jellylike condition, and this is particularly well shown by some types of slime molds (myxomycetes). When one of these is touched the whole organism suddenly sets into a gel formation, and only after the passage of time does the organism gradually pass into a viscid fluid state again.

The ground substance of the protoplasm is known as hyaloplasm and contains a number of bodies and structures, vacuoles, and so on and also a number of very tiny particles, some of them ranging into the ultramicroscopic level and which undergo active Brownian movement. According to Wilson "Flemming observed the dance of minute fat drops in living cartilage cells." Many of the theories of the nature of protoplasm developed in the latter part of the 19th century. At first there were not many theories about its structure because living cytoplasm is optically homogeneous or empty, and between the years 1870 and 1890, when great interest was taken in examinations of fixed and stained tissues, a number of theories of the structure of protoplasm were developed based on its appearance after various types of fixation. Probably one of the most well-known of these is the fibrillar theory. This held that the protoplasm was made up fundamentally of delicate fibrils which were were either separate strands or formed a meshwork and this was situated within a homogeneous, optically empty, ground substance. Among the people whose names were associated with this theory were Leidig, Flemming, Carnoy, and Heidenhain. These fibrils were thought to be of fundamental importance to the vital activities of the cell. However, later on, the fibrillar theory became subdivided into two subsidiary theories. One was the reticular theory and the other the filar theory.

The reticular theory was a modification of the filar theory in the sense that whereas the fibrils did not form networks in the filar theory, they did in the reticular theory. However, toward the end of the century a number of workers including Flemming, Bütschli, and Fischer showed that coagulation artifacts could produce all the phenomena which had been described as fibrillar structures in the cytoplasm. A number of experiments had been carried out by various workers in which every conceivable type of fibrillar structure which had been described in the cell had been

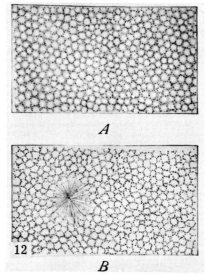

FIG. 12. *The structure of cytoplasm. The alveolar theory. A, Appearance of living cytoplasm of the starfish (Asterias), B, appearance of the cytoplasm after fixation with sublimate acetic. (From "The Cell in Development and Heredity," E. B. Wilson, Macmillan, 1928.)*

duplicated in non-living material made up, for instance, of white of egg or gelatine which had been coagulated by various fixatives. Thus by the end of the 19th century, the fibrillar theory and its offshoots were beginning to fall into disrepute.

Another theory of the structure of protoplasm was the alveolar or foam theory (see Fig. 12) which was enunciated by Bütschli in a series of papers, the first of which he published in 1878. He believed that protoplasm was made up of a series of what he described as "alveolar spheres" which were suspended in a hyaloplasmic material. He regarded protoplasm as being equivalent to two viscid liquids, one of them forming the walls of the spheres scattered amongst the continuous substance (the hyaloplasm). There were also present in the cytoplasm a number of very small granules described as "microsomes," and we should note that the term "microsomes" as used by the early cytologists is quite different from the use of the term today. Nowadays "microsomes" have a fairly specific connotation since they are those bodies which are spun down in an ultracentrifuge from cell homogenates; the last of all the particles of the cell to be spun out. To what extent all modern microsomes represent something which really occurs in the living cell or not we shall discuss later on.

Another theory which developed in the 19th century was the "granule" theory. This was introduced by Altmann in three papers in 1886, 1890, and 1894 and was subsequently developed by quite a number of other writers, mainly Benda and Meves. Altmann, using a special technique, demonstrated red staining fuchsinophil granules in all the cells he examined. In many cases they were a fairly uniform size and in some cells they were very closely crowded and appeared to occupy nearly all the cytoplasm. Altmann regarded these granules as elementary organisms and he called them "cytoblasts" or "bioblasts" and believed that they "lived" in a homogeneous ground substance again called the "hyaloplasm." We know now, of course, that Altmann's granules

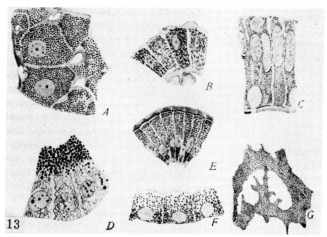

FIG. 13. *Granular structure of cytoplasm as demonstrated by Altmann. We know now these are mostly mitochondria. A, Liver of
mouse; B, tubules of mesonephros, embryo chick; C, intestinal
epithelium of frog; D, pancreas of* Triton *showing secretory granules
and fibrils; E, epithelium of intestinal villus, cat; F, Harderian gland
of rat; G, small portion of pigment cell with pigment granules,
salamander larva. (From "The Cell in Development and Heredity,"
E. B. Wilson, Macmillan, 1928.)*

were actually mitochondria. (See Fig. 13.) Wilson in 1928
summing up the theories of cytoplasmic structure said "we
are driven by a hundred reasons to conclude that the protoplasm has an organization that is perfectly definite but it
is one that finds visible expression in a protean variety of
structures. We are not in a position to regard any of these
as universally diagnostic of the living substance." He went
on to say that the fundamental structure of protoplasm lay
beyond the then limits of microscopic vision. His final
conclusion was that protoplasm possessed an ultrastructural
configuration known as a "metastructure."

The attempts to demonstrate definite structure in protoplasm were followed by a reaction against the alveolar,
fibrillar, and granular theories and led back again to the

extreme reverse conception that the material was structureless. Yet during this pre phase-contrast, pre electron-microscope period, some prophets were found amongst the biochemists who are, or at any rate *were* not noteworthy for
having a morphological outlook on cells. These prophets
demanded the presence of a cytoskeleton which they felt
was a necessary structure along which various enzymes, etc.,
should become aligned. One of the first steps which helped
to bring back to the conception that structure existed in
apparent hyaloplasmic cytoplasm was the development of
the phase-contrast microscope in which a number of formed
structures were seen to exist in the cytoplasm of the living
cell.

Immediately beneath the cell membrane, the protoplasm
of the cell is differentiated to form an "ectoplasm" which
appears to be in a partly gelled condition. It is probable
that this ectoplasm plays an important part in the movements of the cell, and it appears to be actively forming
and reforming in the movement of protocells such as the
Amoeba. It is also modified to form cilia. These are, in
effect, ectoplasmic prolongations surrounded by a cell membrane. The ectoplasm is also a constituent part of the
microvilli which occur on absorbent cells of the kidney
tubules and intestine.

Phase-contrast microscopy demonstrated a good deal of
structure in the apparent hyaloplasm, and later this was
supported by the results obtained with a further development of this sort of microscopy—the interference microscope
in which objects of different density in the cell were colored
differently according to their density. More recently the
electron microscope, using the excellent fixation produced
by osmium tetroxide has demonstrated an incredible complexity in what was only a few years ago thought of as a
relatively homogeneous hyaloplasm.

The cytoplasm is filled with mitochondria, microbodies
of various sorts, double membranes, Golgi apparatus, and
various granules; in fact, there is relatively little of what

we might describe as hyaloplasm. This hyaloplasm does, however, exist and when fixed and examined under the electron microscope it seems to be composed of an extremely fine network and this becomes coarser or finer according to the type of fixative used. Now what is this network composed of? Wykoff has pointed out that a number of proteins which contain long, flamentous type molecules (see Fig. 14) are capable of forming gels which have many of the physicochemical properties characteristic of protoplasm. He points out that gelatin is one of these and describes one of his experiments in which gelatin gels were first fixed with osmic acid and then examined under the electron microscope. He found that the gelatin was arranged in a network and that the pores of the net were small or large according to the concentration of the gelatin/gel or the fixative used. With a concentration of 2 to 4% in a gel, the net which results possesses a pore size which is very similar to that found in cells, but the pores get smaller if the gel is more concentrated. It is probable therefore that the network-like structure of the hyaloplasm which we see is really to some extent the effect of the fixative, although it is partly the expression of the nature and distribution of the filamentous molecules of protein which form the basis of the hyaloplasm. These molecules are, in fact, probably arranged in a sort of network, a structure that Sir Rudolph Peters once described as the "cytoskeleton," and which he thought was the basis of cytoplasmic structure. This suggestion was made some years before the electron microscope demonstrated such a wealth of formed components within the hyaloplasm itself.

Within the network of filamentous molecules (both protein and polysaccharide) which build up the hyaloplasm, a variety of molecules, not only free protein, polysaccharide, and lipid but also ions, move about attaching and detaching themselves to the network in accordance with the electrical and other forces operating at that level (see Fig. 15).

We can, indeed, picture this hyaloplasmic network as a sort of skeleton for the rest of the cell.

Now in this hyaloplasmic structure lie the rest of the cell elements which have to be separated from it to carry out the types of activity in which they specialize.

THE ENDOPLASMIC RETICULUM

A prominent feature of the cytoplasm of cells, particu-

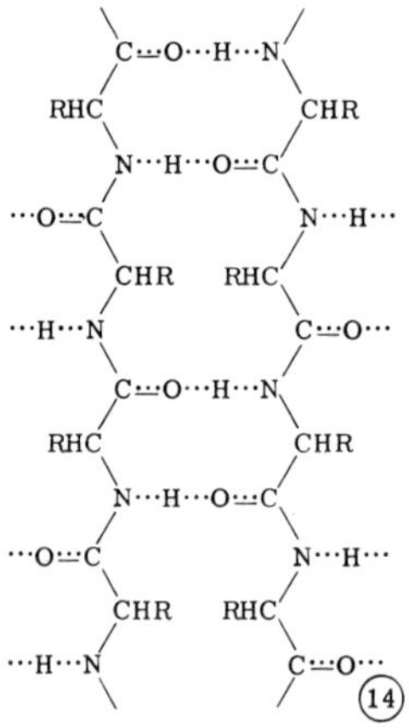

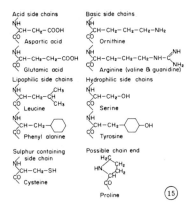

Fig. 14.
Hydrogen bonds between polypeptide chains. (From "Submicroscopic Morphology of Protoplasm and its Derivatives" Frey-Wyssling, 1948, Elsevier.)

Fig. 15.
Side chains "R" of the polypeptide chains. (From "Submicroscopic Morphology of Protoplasm and its Derivatives" Frey-Wyssling, 1948, Elsevier.)

larly pancreatic cells, under the electron microscope, is a basophilic fibrillar structure which takes us back a little into the fibrillar theory of protoplasm; this structure is known either as the "endoplasmic reticulum" or "ergastoplasm" and reference will be made again to these names later on.

The structure and function of this material has been worked out and recognized in the last few years with the aid of the electron microscope, although it was originally discovered a long time ago with the light microscope. The discoverer was Garnier and the year 1897. The material discovered was a basophilic fibrillar material which could be seen in stained cells, particularly in the basal region of gland cells, and it was called by Garnier "ergastoplasm."

The ergastoplasm appears to be part of the system described as the endoplasmic reticulum. This latter structure was described by Porter and Thompson in a paper in 1947 on electron-microscope studies of a chick macrophage (see Fig. 16). The macrophage when very thinly spread out

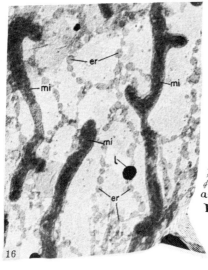

Fig. 16. *Endoplasmic reticulum and mitochondria in tissue culture cells (chick macrophage). er, Endoplasmic reticulum; mi, mitochondria; l, lipid. (Preparation and photograph by Dr. K. Porter. From "General Cytology," De Robertis, Nowinski and Saez, 1960, W. B. Saunders.)*

showed that the cytoplasm was everywhere permeated by a tenuous network which they described as a lacelike reticulum. This they quite understandably called an endoplasmic reticulum. Later on, when fine sectioning of cells became possible in the 1950's, the endoplasmic reticulum seemed to occupy the position that was normally occupied by the "ergastoplasm," as Garnier had called it. In addition it also appeared to spread through the other parts of the cytoplasm of the cell and to be present, to a greater or less extent, in practically all the cells which have been examined. However, at this point we should try to solve the problem of terminology. One of the characteristics of ergastoplasm is that it is basophilic, but not all the endoplasmic reticulum is basophilic although both basophilic and nonbasophilic regions in ultrathin sections of cells have the same double membrane structure. The difference is that the basophilic portions have ribonucleoprotein particles attached to the membranes and the nonbasophilic parts do not. Therefore the ergastoplasm can be thought of as a specialized basophilic part of the endoplasmic reticulum. Sjöstrand tried to avoid this controversy by giving the names of Greek letters to various membranes in the cells. The membranes which form the endoplasmic reticulum he has described as the α-cytomembrane, the membranes of the mitochondria and of the cytoplasm receiving other Greek letters to designate them. Sjöstrand's recommendation for nomenclature, however, seems to be a rather cumbersome method of describing these structures.

The use of the term "ergastoplasm" for the system of cytoplasmic membranes is largely supported by the French school recently headed by the late Charles Oberling, whereas in the United States the accent is more on endoplasmic reticulum with ergastoplasm as a specialized part of it. This is the nomenclature followed by the Rockefeller group headed by Porter and Palade.

Since the nature of the endoplasmic reticulum and, indeed, of many other cell structures is based on electron-microscope studies, we might perhaps briefly consider the significance of electron-microscope pictures, in general, and attempt to assess to what extent they represent a real structural condition in the living cell.

The late Dr. Oberling has listed six points which suggest that the electron-microscope picture is a true picture of the living cell.

1. The types of structures which are seen under the electron microscope have also been seen in living cells, and they have been photographed or filmed by the phase-contrast microscope.

2. Whenever the possibility has existed for comparison of the same cells, for instance, alive as viewed under the phase-contrast microscope or in fixed condition with the electron microscope, there has been perfect aggreement in the picture.

3. The same methods of fixation and observation reveal all the structures side by side and present in all cells, even in those which are very different from both the phylogenetic and the functional points of view. The appearance of these structures depends to a large extent on the perfect preservation of cells by first class fixation.

4. In order to attain excellent pictures the cells must be fixed in the living state. This proves the great sensitivity of the observed structures and the reliability of the procedures in detecting such structural changes which take place immediately after vital functions have ceased.

5. The techniques of homogenization, fractionation, and ultracentrifugation have given the opportunity to isolate these structures and obtain them in a relatively pure condition in sufficient amounts to permit biochemical investigations, thus bringing closer the collaboration between the morphological and biochemical studies of the cell.

6. These structures, as they appear under the electron microscope, do not always produce the same aspect, but they vary according to the evolutionary phases and also differ in pathological conditions from which the cell may have been suffering.

These points are very strong ones and possibly the
strongest of all from the point of view of the very delicate
structure which is demonstrated in electron microscopy is
point 4. With regard to the first three, very few people
have ever doubted that, for instance, mitochondria (as
seen with the light microscope) existed in living cells. They
have been seen in living as well as in fixed cells examined
by the optical microscope, and it was no surprise to find
that they were also present in electron-microscope pictures.
The point that has been really at issue is whether the
extremely fine structures which the electron microscopists
demonstrate do really exist in life. The very fine, double
membrane structures and so on, could possibly be produced
as a result of the technique used, although in view of the
widespread constancy of findings this is unlikely. Nevertheless we should still keep a healthy attitude of caution in
accepting all these fine structural details and be prepared
to alter our views should evidence accumulate that there
are errors in this depiction of ultrafine structure. At the
moment, however, it appears that the electron microscope
is telling the truth so far as we can interpret it, but that
it is not yet showing everything that is in the cell.

Garnier, the discoverer of ergastoplasm, brought out some
very important points concerning its nature and these have
been listed in an excellent article by Haguenau (Int. Rev.
of Cytol., Vol. VII) to which the reader is referred for
further details of the ergastoplasm. Garnier, according to
Haguenau, said that, in the basal region of all cells, without
exception, there was a portion of the cytoplasm which
seemed to have a fibrillar or rodlike structure, that these
filaments or rods were not separate structures but were
actually part of the cytoplasm and were in direct continuity with it. Haguenau points out that the electron
microscope has provided an excellent confirmation of this.
Garnier also said that these filaments were stained by basic
dyes—those used were safranin gentian violet and toluidine
blue—and that the intensity with which this basic staining

occurred varied with the stage of secretion in gland cells. Another point which he made was that the ergastoplasm was not a permanent structure and that its development was related directly to the state of activity of the cell. He said, for instance, that in gland cells the filaments appeared much more numerous when the cell, having already gone through a cycle of secretion and excretion, was preparing a new cycle. When the cell became loaded again with secretory granules, the filaments became less obvious and disappeared. His final point was that the filaments were closely related from a topographical point of view with the nucleus, that masses of the material formed laterally on the sides of the nucleus, and that sometimes the latter was completely encircled by the ergastoplasm. Garnier also thought that nuclear sap or chromatic substance originating from the nucleolus was able to pass through the nuclear membrane and enter into association with the ergastoplasm. This was actually a very significant comment as will be seen later.

Following Garnier's work many other authors figured and described and categorized the ergastoplasm. Prenant in 1898 wrote a review on the ergastoplasm which he called the "protoplasme supérieur." He described the ergastoplasm as a very important zone of the cytoplasm which was capable of differentiating into specific structures and among these, according to Haguenau, were included the "Nebenkern," the "Dotterkern" of the germ cell and the ergastoplasm of the gland cell and even the Nissl bodies of nerve cells. These were rather interesting conclusions since they have now been supported by electron-microscope studies. Haguenau has pointed out that in the history of most discoveries there is a period in which it is first described, then a lot of other people describe it, and finally there is a period when everybody believes it is an artifact due to fixation. She points out that at about the same time as the ergastoplasm was discovered Altmann discovered mitochondria, but comments made on the latter by Benda in 1898 and 1899 served to complicate the proper interpretation and acceptance of the ergastoplasm. Haguenau divided the post-Garnier workers into three groups: the first group were represented by Morelle in 1927 who claimed that the ergastoplasm was nothing more than modified ground cytoplasm which took up basic stains, this being due not to any difference in structure but simply to a chemical difference. He claimed that this area of the cytoplasm was never really fibrillar. Then there was a second group who thought that the ergastoplasm was only mitochondria which were distorted in shape. Champy in 1911, for example, stated that mitochondria and ergastoplasm were one and the same and that the preparations which showed ergastoplasm were simply preparations with poorer fixation than those which showed mitochondria. To some extent there is some justification for this point of view, since mitochondria and ergastoplasm are so closely related to each other topographically that it is natural enough for a mitochondrial stain to demonstrate concentrations of mitochondria in the same site as the ergastoplasm. The third group agreed with Garnier that mitochondria and ergastoplasm were quite different structures but these, according to Haguenau had to fight very hard to prove it. Prominent amongst these was Regaud.

The critical experiment which Regaud published in 1908 was one in which he showed that, if he had acetic acid in his fixative, there were no mitochondria in the preparation but the ergastoplasm appeared quite normal. On the other hand, with acetic acid absent mitochondria could be demonstrated very conveniently but the ergastoplasm did not take up its normal appearance. Haguenau quotes Re-

FIG. 17. *Endoplasmic reticulum of liver cell showing double membrane structure and RNA granules on the outside of membrane pairs. Transverse section, fine structure of mitochondria can be seen. (**Preparation and photograph by Michael Sheridan, Anatomy Department, Emory University**.)*

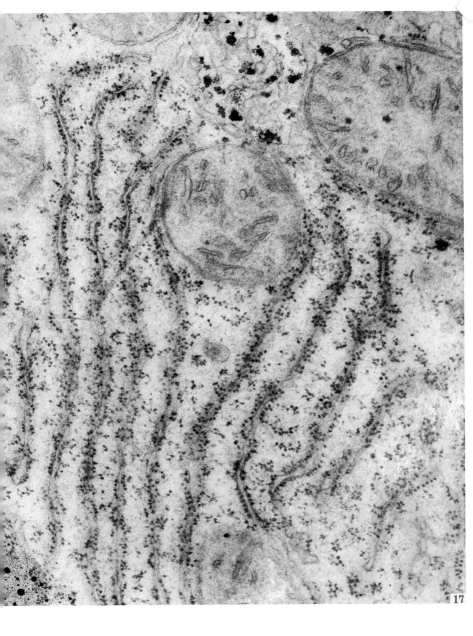

17

gaud (1909), "It is possible that the ergastoplasm consists of a protoplasmic support impregnated with chromatin or a closely related substance." Rees in 1940 using the polarizing microscope made a study of the ergastoplasm and came to the conclusion that there was a homogeneous filamentous structure present in the cytoplasm of living cells, but it was the electron microscope which finally confirmed and helped to delineate the structure of the ergastoplasm.

Preliminary studies by Porter and colleagues leading to the designation of this material as endoplasmic reticulum have already been mentioned. In 1950, Hillier was probably the first person to demonstrate that, in fine sections of liver, fine fibrous matter is present in the cytoplasm of the cell, but he was not able to establish its identity. Dalton in the same year also produced electron micrographs which demonstrated quite clearly that the cytoplasm contained a number of filamentous units and that these tended to be grouped in particular areas and were reduced following fasting of the animal.

The work of the French and American schools, together with contributions by the Swedish school headed by Sjö-strand, have now established a great deal of interesting information about the structure, nature, identity, and distribution of the endoplasmic reticulum and its specialized part, the ergastoplasm.

The endoplasmic reticulum appears fibrous in nature in sections and it is of interest that these fibers appear to form pairs, and they have been regarded, in fact, as paired membranes (see Fig. 17). Actually, it seems that they are in many cases the walls of membraneous tubules or even sac-like structures or vesicles and are frequently referred to as double membranes. It is of interest that these membranes show the 75–80-A unit structure which is so characteristic of cell membranes and which may be significant in the light of something we will say later on about them. There is some discrepancy between the findings of electron microscopists regarding the ergastoplasm and the

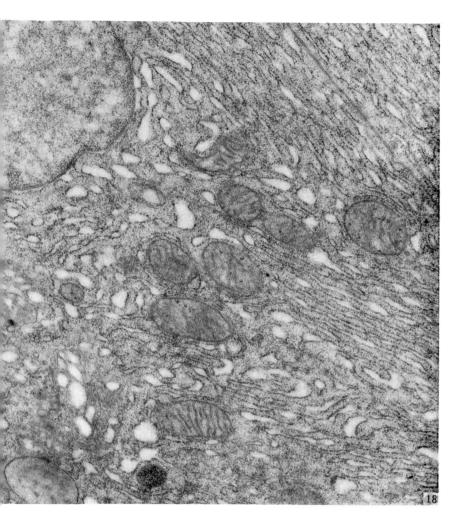

Fig. 18. *Portion pancreatic acinar cell. Several mitochondria can be seen. The complex nature of the endoplasmic reticulum is obvious. A portion of the nucleus can be seen on the upper left, note the double structure of the nuclear membrane. (Preparation and photograph by R. Quinton Cox, Dept. of Anatomy, Emory Univ.)*

findings of the classical cytologists. The latter claim that
the basophilic staining with which these fibrillar structures
are associated appears to be localized at the basal end of
the cell, whereas with the electron microscope these fibers
or membranes extend all through the cell. This, however,
can be explained in part by the fact that it is only when
there are quite a number of membranes close together that
they show up as a strongly basophilic area under the light
microscope, and in other parts of the cell the membranes
are more widely spread out and are not organized in dense
groups; therefore the characteristic staining reaction is
spread out over a great area of the cytoplasm and becomes
diluted. Furthermore some of the membranes do not have
ribonucleic acid granules attached to them (the component
which produces the basophilic staining) and are called
"smooth" endoplasmic reticulum. It is also evident that
some endoplasmic reticulum membranes may show as basophilic structures but do not have any obvious RNA granules
—so, perhaps, this material can be associated with the
endoplasmic reticulum in a molecular as well as a particulate form.

In areas where the ergastoplasmic membranes are concentrated together so that the whole cytoplasm has a lamellar
appearance, it has been suggested that the term "organized
ergastoplasm" should be used (see Fig. 18). This term was
suggested by Houdson and Ham in 1955. Another interesting organization of the ergastoplasm is the "Nebenkern."
Nebenkern are structures which are basophilic in nature.
Their significance and method of formation was unknown
to older cytologists, but under the electron microscope it
appears that they are concentric layers of ergastoplasmic
membranes which in section look like an onion bulb or,
as some authors put it, a finger-print. It is possible that these
structures may originate from mitochondria. The ergastoplasm may also be modified in nerve cells in the region
where Nissl bodies are found, as demonstrated by Palay and
Palade. There are considerable variations in amount of

ergastoplasm which is thought to be related to the differentiation of cells, and it has been suggested that it may also be linked to growth. There seems little doubt that the membranes are linked to function, and they are particularly obvious in cells which are engaged in the production of protein.

Noteworthy also about the structure of ergastoplasm is the association with it of a large number of granules (see Fig. 19). It is of interest that these granules are associated with the outer part of the membrane. The side of the membrane directed toward the cavity which the membrane lines in the cytoplasm is smooth and has no granules attached to it, whereas on the cytoplasmic side of the membrane, quite distinct granules are found. They are basophilic in nature, range from approximately 120 to 150 A in diameter and have been the subject of considerable speculation. Since they are basophilic in nature, it is obvious that they are, as mentioned earlier, the cause of the basophilic staining of the ergastoplasm recorded by the older cytologists. The studies by Palade and Siekewitz over the last five or six years have demonstrated the very interesting fact that these granules are composed of ribonucleic acid combined with protein. The way in which Palade and Siekewitz obtained this information is of interest. They treated homogenates of cells with deoxycholate, a surface-tension reducing agent which detached the granules from the membranes. Then they were able, by differential centrifugation, to isolate a number of them, carry out chemical analyses, and so establish that they were largely composed of ribonucleic acid. However, one should not think that all the ribonucleic acid in the cytoplasm is associated with the endoplasmic reticulum. It is present in other parts of the cell as well, but there is some evidence that about 25% of the cytoplasmic ribonucleic acid is, in fact, associated with the endoplasmic reticulum.

One of the interesting observations about these particles, demonstrating perhaps not so much division of labor in

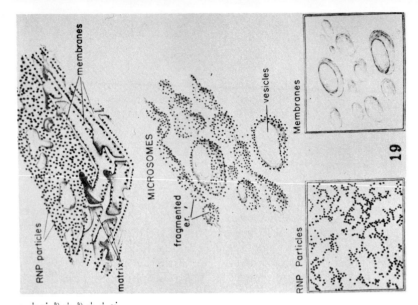

Fig. 19 (right). Endoplasmic reticulum showing relationship of ribonucleoprotein particles to the E.R. membranes. The other illustrations demonstrate the nature of the microsomes derived from the fragmentation of the endoplasmic reticulum. Treatment of these microsomes separates the two constituents demonstrated in the lower two figures. (From "General Cytology," De Robertis, Nowinski and Saez, 1960, W. B. Saunders.)

Fig. 20 (below, left). Diagram of a hypothetic cell according to Robertson. He says: "The cell membrane is shown as a pair of dense lines separated by a light interzone. The invaginations of the cell surface known as caveolae intracellulares (c.i.) are indicated in several areas. Some of these extend for a considerable distance into the cell and they may connect with the endoplasmic reticulum (e.r.). The nuclear membrane is composed of flattened sacs of the endoplasmic reticulum, and by means of the nuclear pores nucleoplasm (nuc.) is in continuity with cytoplasm. The Golgi apparatus (G) is here shown as a modified component of the endoplasmic reticulum Secretion granules (g) are shown as dense aggregates contained within membranes of the endoplasmic reticulum. Nucleo-protein granules (n.p.g.) are shown scattered through the cytoplasm and in some regions attached to the cytoplasmic surfaces of membranes of the endoplasmic reticulum. . . . One mitochondrion (m.) is shown with its cristae formed by invagination of its inner membrane." (From "Structure and Function of Sub-cellular Components" Robertson, Biochemical Society Symposia, 1959, Cambridge Univ. Press.)

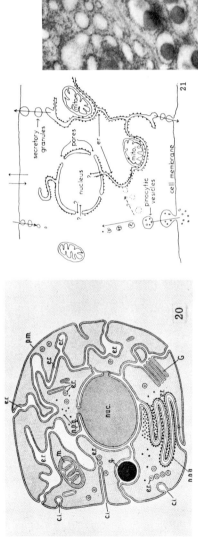

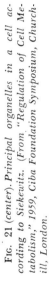

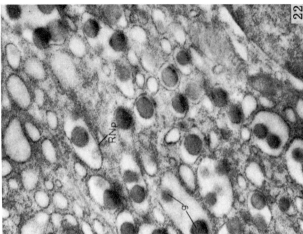

FIG. 21 (center). *Principal organelles in a cell according to Siekevitz. (From "Regulation of Cell Metabolism," 1959, Ciba Foundation Symposium, Churchill, London.)*

FIG. 22 (right). *Intracisternal granules in the basal region of an acinar cell of guinea pig pancreas; g, intracisternal granules inside vesicles of the E.R. These vesicles are bounded by membranes having attached ribonucleoprotein particles (RNp.). (Illustration and legend from Palade and Siekewitz. 1956, J. Biophys. Biochem. Cytol. 2, 671.)*

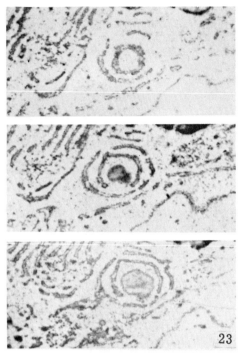

FIG. 23. *Membranes are shown presumably produced from nuclear membrane and surrounding secretion granules. (From Gay, "Nuclear Control of the Cell," Scientific American, January 1960.)*

FIG. 24 *(opposite, left). Showing a bleblike excrescence from the nuclear membrane (from cell of salivary gland of larval fruit fly) which is believed by Gay to form endoplasmic reticulum by budding off from the nucleus. The bleb is situated on the far right side of the nuclear membrane and a number of E.R. membranes can be seen close to and parallel to it. (From Gay, "Nuclear Control of the Cell," Scientific American, January 1960.)*

FIG. 25 *(opposite, right). Diagrammatic drawing of origin of endoplasmic reticulum from the nuclear membrane (see Fig. 24). (From Gay, "Nuclear Control of the Cell," Scientific American, January 1960.)*

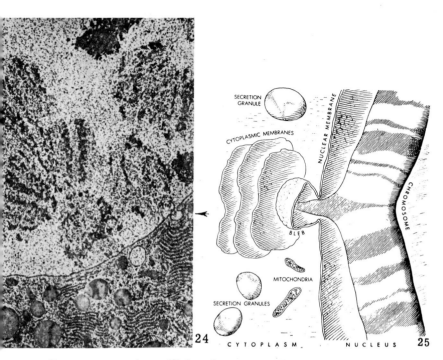

cells as co-operation of labor between cell constituents, is
that in the nucleolus, ribonucleic acid particles are found
which are the same size (150 A in diameter as those associated with the endoplasmic reticulum (see Figs. 21 and 22).
(It is of interest, also, that the deoxyribonucleic acid particles which are found in the chromatin of the nucleus are
also about 150 A in diameter.) It seems possible that the
RNA particles could pass out from the nucleolus through
pores present in the nuclear membranes (which we will talk
about later) and become attached to the walls of the endoplasmic reticulum. The fact that there is a coincidence in
size is of very great interest from this point of view. A different type of migration has also been suggested by Gay
who showed with the electron microscope that blebs form-

ing at the surface of nuclei may become converted into endoplasmic reticulum and that RNA granules appeared to become attached to them before they actually became detached from the nucleus (see Figs. 23, 24, and 25).

THE NATURE OF MICROSOMES

When Claude applied Bensley's technique of differential centrifugation to cells, isolated different cellular components, and subjected them to chemical analysis, he described a series of minute bodies which are submicroscopic in size, i.e., below the limit of the resolution by the optical microscope. He described these bodies as microsomes. They are the smallest bodies in cellular homogenates and come down after everything has been centrifuged off, i.e., at the highest speed of centrifugation, leaving only the supernatant. Many chemical studies were done on the microsomes and a good deal of information on their enzymes and chemical composition was obtained. However, one thing which made cytologists and particularly electron microscopists uneasy was the fact that, if one looked at a liver cell (which Claude used largely as the source of material for the production of microsomes) under the electron microscope, nothing could be seen in the cytoplasm which bore any resemblance to the microsomes. Since these were of a size which could be seen at the magnification used by the electron microscope, it was difficult to understand where they came from in the homogenates. The microsomes contain a good deal of ribonucleic acid and so does the ergastoplasm. Finally, by isolating the pellet of microsomes centrifuged out from the homogenized cells and by examining ultrathin sections of them under the electron microscope, various workers showed that the microsomes were small vesicles with ribonucleic acid granules attached to them. It thus seemed quite obvious that the grinding-up of the cell during homogenization broke up the endoplasmic reticulum and the bits formed themselves into little vesicles which floated in the fluid and were finally centrifuged down. This work was first done by Slatterbach in 1953 and subsequently by Palade and his colleagues. (See Fig. 19.)

Relation of endoplasmic reticulum membranes
to cell membrane

The E.R. (endoplasmic reticulum) membranes have a structure (as mentioned in Chapter I) which is similar in structure and dimensions to the cell membrane. It has been suggested that the E.R. membranes might represent complex infoldings of the cell membrane and that the cavities between the folds of the membranes may be in direct continuity with the exterior of the cell. We know that some infoldings occur, they have been mentioned before and are known as the caveolae intracellulares. These structures have a space of constant size between the two folds of cell membrane which form their walls—this space is 200 A in width, thus the total width of the system including the two membranes of 80 A thickness each is about 360 A (according to Porter). Now, in some parts of the cell the membranes and spaces of the endoplasmic reticulum approach this dimension, but there is tremendous variation in the space (known as the "cisternal space") between the membranes, in parts it may be greatly dilated. This suggests that the endoplasmic reticulum is not necessarily part of the same system to which the caveolae intracellulares belong. No certain connection between the E.R. membrane systems and the cell membrane has been established although the possibility exists, and Porter and other authors have recognized that the connection may not be permanent but that it may be spasmodic. A distinct possibility occurs also that the endoplasmic reticulum developed originally from infoldings of the cell membrane, that it then increased in complexity, and finally lost its connection with its point or points of origin, but temporary direct connection between the cisternae of the endoplasmic reticulum and the exterior of the cell can occur. (See Figs. 20 and 21 for summary of cell structure.)

It is thus possible that the cavity between the membranes in the E.R. represents a path by means of which the contents of the membranes or sacs (cisternae) can be excreted to the exterior. In other words the secretory products of the cell pass from the cytoplasm through the walls possibly in molecular form, collect into droplets in the interior of the membranes, and pass along them. It is, of course, possible that secretion products form in the cisternae (see Fig. 22). In 1957, Hendler and colleagues found that, in the gland cells which produce albumen in the hen oviduct, the cavities or spaces between the membranes were dilated and contained a precipitate which possessed the staining and other characters of the secreted material which is found in the lumen of the gland. There is other evidence to indicate too that, possibly, these spaces between the membranes represent a pathway for secretory material. It is of interest, as shown by Brandes that, in the ventral lobe of the prostate gland in mice and rats, the spaces between the pairs of membranes are so enormously dilated that the membranes from opposite pairs come into close apposition with each other; pairs of membranes still exist but they are the halves of opposite pairs which have come together. The space between the original pairs of membranes is packed with an amorphous material. The ribonucleic acid granules in the such pairs of membranes are, of course, on the inside instead of the outside as they were when the original halves of the pairs were together. It is possible that this enormous accumulation of material in these endoplasmic sacs really represent accumulation of secretion. It is of interest that, if the animals are castrated, the pairs of membranes with the granules on the inside separate from each other, the amount of secretory material appears to decrease, and the original halves of the membrane pairs come close together again so that the ribonucleic acid granules can now be seen on the outside. Brandes has also demonstrated that, by injection or implantation of male sex hormone, the original state of the cell could be produced again. This is in a sense an

"Alice Through the Looking-Glass" type of cell in which the normal arrangement of cytoplasm and endoplasmic reticulum spaces is reversed. When this cell is in its normal condition, the spaces between the membranes contain, in fact, the strands of cytoplasm and by far the main body of the cell is occupied by what are presumably the secretion products.

It has probably not been made clear up to date that all these endoplasmic sacs are probably continuous with each other and thus form a convoluted system of spaces coursing through the cytoplasm of the cell. It appears, also, that folds of the endoplasmic reticulum constitute the nuclear membrane (this will be discussed later). Since this membrane has been shown to contain pores, it is quite possible that material could pass from the nucleus into the cisternae and along these channels to the exterior of the cell without having to traverse the cytoplasm or the cell membrane at all. A possible origin of the endoplasmic reticulum from the nucleus is shown by Figs. 23–25.

At this point we should enlarge a little on the subject of the caveolae intracellulares. These were originally described by Yamada as consisting of a number of infoldings of the surface membrane of some cells. He found them in endoneurial, endothelial, pulmonary epithelial, and muscle cells. Although it is possible that these caveolae could, in fact, represent the regions where the E.R. channels communicate with the exterior, the existing evidence is against this. If this were so then there is a continuous, if extremely tortuous, pathway which stems from the vicinity of the nuclear membrane extending to the exterior of the cell and which could be described as a possible circulatory system for the cell. At the moment it seems most likely that the caveolae represent only blind pockets which extend for variable distances into the cells, and there is no evidence that they are actually continuous with the ergastoplasm. Palade has suggested that these invaginations in endothelial cells, at any rate, represent stages in a process of what is described as "micropinocytosis" which has already been discussed. It has been suggested that when these little vesicles containing water pass into the cell, the cell membrane then dissolves away and the water is liberated into the cytoplasm. This conception of the cell membrane "pinching off" and a little vesicle passing into the cytoplasm is attractive, but one of the difficulties of accepting it is the mechanism of the formation of the vesicle. We know that the cell membrane can invaginate in this way (it has been seen to do so) but whether, when the membranes on the two sides of the vesicle bend around and come in contact with each other, they are, in fact, capable of coalescing and nipping off a vesicle is another matter. It has been pointed out that, if the membrane of a cell was a purely lipid substance, there would be no difficulty at all in such a concept, but, since the outside and probably the inside parts of the lipid membrane of a cell are covered with protein, this would make such a coalescence rather difficult to conceive from a physicochemical point of view. On the other hand, an invagination of the membrane may draw off a little droplet of water and the membrane may then burst internally and squirt the drop of water into the cell, and then there would be no difficulty in the burst sides of the membrane joining up in the usual way. This seems to the present author to be a much more likely way for pinocytosis to take place than for a vesicle to be actually cut off.

The Golgi apparatus has also been shown to be composed of double membrane structures without, however, the associated ribonucleoprotein granules of the endoplasmic reticulum. Although we will be dealing with the Golgi apparatus later on, we might mention here the concept which has been put forward by some authors that the Golgi apparatus represents a part of the system of the endoplasmic reticulum and that it is in communication with it. We do not know whether the whole of the endoplasmic reticulum is in continuous communication with itself, however, if it is and if the Golgi apparatus is part of it, then it is possible to assume that everything passing along the cisternae of the reticulum will have to filter through the Golgi region. It should be stressed that there is no proof that this is so, that many cytologists believe it is not so, but that such a possibility exists.

One problem which should be discussed at this point is the origin of the endoplasmic reticulum. Where in fact does it come from? There are many controversial theories on this subject. It has been suggested that it might originate as an infolding or infoldings of the cell membrane, and this theory was put forward by Palade.

The Nebenkern because of its high concentration of E.R. membranes might be considered as a possible region in the cytoplasm where this material is being formed. The Nebenkern is made up of a dense aggregation of concentric rings, and one could, perhaps, consider the possibility of the membranes peeling off from such a germ center. The same sort of appearance has also been noted in association with the nuclear membrane and has led to the suggestion that the endoplasmic reticulum is formed in this region and that the layers are, in fact, peeling off the nuclear membrane (see also Figs. 23–25). However it may quite easily be interpreted the opposite way, i.e., the close apposition of the existing ergastoplasm around the nuclear membrane may be a part of the complex canalicular system which permits an almost direct passage through the nuclear membrane direct into the cisternae of the reticulum. Again, there are a number of authors who think the endoplasmic reticulum is associated with mitochondria. There is no doubt that many pictures of mitochondria, closely surrounded by concentric layers of endoplasmic reticulum have been obtained, and we, ourselves, have found this particularly well demonstrated around the mitochondria of the liver cells of scorbutic guinea pigs. In some cases, Sheridan in this department has found a tremendous concentration of many layers of reticulum around the mitochondria, as though, in fact, the reticulum is being formed on the surface of the mitochondrial membrane and is being split off. Rouiller and his colleagues have demonstrated that, in animals which have been poisoned, the endoplasmic reticulum, destroyed or badly damaged by the treatment, always reappears in association with mitochondria. The membranes of the reticulum may not undergo direct physical formation in the sense that the membranes are produced on the surface of the mitochondrial membrane and split off; it may be that the mitochondria supply the energy necessary for the production of these membranes. Furthermore the close relationship between the endoplasmic reticulum and the mitochondria may simply be physiological, that is they are co-operating in some metabolic process such as the synthesis of protein. However, the origin of the endoplasmic reticulum is a problem which is far from solved, and we must await further evidence before drawing a conclusion.

CHAPTER IV

Mitochondria

known for many years. They were first discovered and described by Altmann in 1886, and were put more or less definitely on the cytological map by Benda in 1903. They can be easily demonstrated with suitable dyes. Altmann's aniline fuchsine–picric acid technique shows them up very well. Regaud's iron–hematoxylin method is also very good. The mitochondria can even be seen in the living cell by staining them intravitally with Janus green and, of course, they show up extremely well with the phase-contrast and interference microscopes. There is not much difficulty, then, in establishing their existence and nature. Their dimensions vary, of course, but they range in most cells from about 0.5 to 2μ or longer. The filamentous mitochondria, for example, which are present in connective tissue cells may be much longer than this. Extremely small, and even submicroscopic mitochondria may also exist. Extremely small-sized mitochondria are, in fact, known, and Rhodin (1954) has described structures ranging from 0.1 to 0.5μ which are presumably mitochondrial in nature. Green has pointed out that the various enzymes and proteins which mitochondria contain can be accommodated in a very much smaller particle than any known mitochondria and still perform all the functions required of them. Some of these much

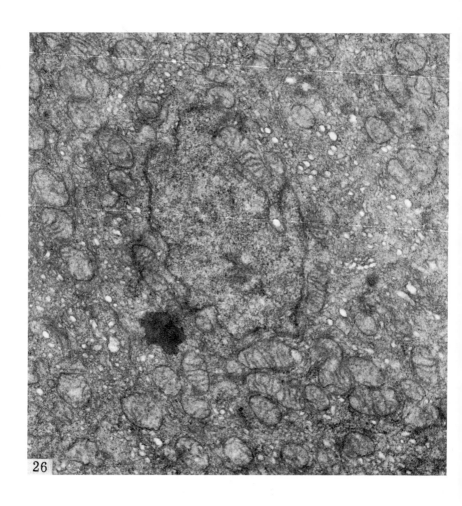

26

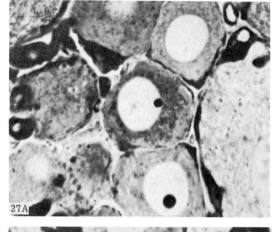

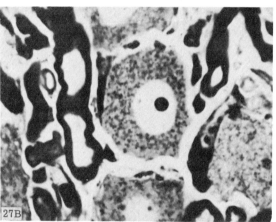

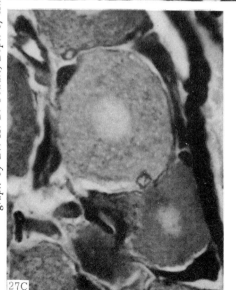

Fig. 26 (above). Cell from guinea-pig liver showing mitochondrion surrounded by fold of nuclear membrane demonstrating close contact between nucleus and mitochondria. Other mitochondria may be seen close to the nucleus. (Preparation and photograph by Michael Sheridan, Dept. of Anatomy, Emory Univ.)

Fig. 27 (below). Relation between nucleolus and mitochondria in spinal ganglion neurons. A, Nucleolus in contact with nuclear membrane and mitochondria congregated around nucleus especially on the side where the nucleolus is touching; B, nucleolus in center of nucleus and mitochondria scattered through the cytoplasm; C, decrease in number of mitochondria and presence of many vacuoles of unidentified material, faint diffuse stain by nucleus). It is of interest that the nucleolus reacts with the same intensity as the mitochondria to the Regaud technique. Presumably this indicates that it contains a similar lipoprotein complex. (Preparation and photograph by Dr. H. B. Tewari, Dept. of Anatomy, Emory Univ.)

smaller mitochondria may not have all the details of organization of larger mitochondria but there is no reason why
they should not contain all the enzymes and other compounds which are important for mitochondrial structure
and function.

It is of interest to note that, in living tissue culture cells,
the mitochondria undergo continuous movement. This has
been noted by quite a number of workers, and the movements have been described frequently. These movements
may be fitful individual movements by the mitochondrion
itself, i.e., bending, wriggling, and writhing, or may consist
of movement of the whole mitochondrion through the cytoplasm of the cell. The cause of the bending and twisting
movements of the mitochondria is not exactly known. At
one time it was thought to result from the contracting of
the polypeptide chains which are part of the membrane of
the mitochondria. It may be due to the fact that the mitochondria were engaged in active ion pumping or being
twisted by cytoplasmic movements. In the second type of
movement in which there is a transport of the whole mitochondrion from one part of the cell to another, the movement is possibly related to streaming movements of the
cytoplasm or to electrical forces. The mitochondria have
been described as making journeys from the cell membrane
to the nuclear membrane and back again almost as if they
were discharging either an electric charge or even perhaps
some compound on the membrane that they touch. There
are also records that, when the mitochondria come in contact with the nuclear membrane (see Fig. 26) the nucleolus
sometimes moves across the cell and comes in contact with
the nuclear membrane at the same point at which the
mitochondrion is touching it, and this suggests that there
may be some exchange of compounds or substances during
this period. This has been demonstrated in spinal ganglion
cells by Dr. Tewari in the author's laboratory (see Figs.
27 (a, b and c). Filamentous mitochondria have frequently
been observed to break up into batonettes and these have

been observed to break up into granules. The reverse process has also been found to occur, granules have been seen to join up into batonettes and these into longer filamentous mitochondria. What the significance of this breaking up is we do not know, but a little later we will refer to this process again in the light of what will be said about the metabolic activities of mitochondria.

When mitochondria were studied in ultrathin sections of tissue, it was found by Palade in 1953, Sjöstrand, 1953, and by Rhodin in 1954, that they had an interesting internal structure (see Figs. 28 and 29). These workers found first of all that there was a single membrane round the outside, that inside this membrane was another membrane so that the two made a double membrane and, after a little controversy, it was agreed that the inner of these two membranes was extended to form a number of bars or plates which projected into the interior of the mitochondria, in some cases touching or almost touching the other side. These plates or bars or tubes had double structure again, since they were a reflection of the inner membrane of the mitochondria. They were described by Palade as the "cristae mitochondriales" (see Figs. 30 and 31). Changes in these cristae appear to be related to function, for instance Palade has drawn attention to the fact that the amount of cytochrome in the mitochondrial fraction of a homogenate is directly related to the number of cristae present in the mitochondria. When metabolic activity is high, for example, in rapidly contracting skeletal and heart muscle, the mitochondria have many densely packed cristae. In smooth muscle, however, where the activity is greatly reduced, the cristae present in the mitochondria are relatively sparse. There are claims that, e.g., in mouse tumor cells and in paramecium, cristae may be everted into the cytoplasm. Presumably in this case the outer membrane is folded into cristae.

It is of interest that the double membranes which surround the mitochondria show the same 80 A unit structure which is characteristic of the cell membrane, and Robertson

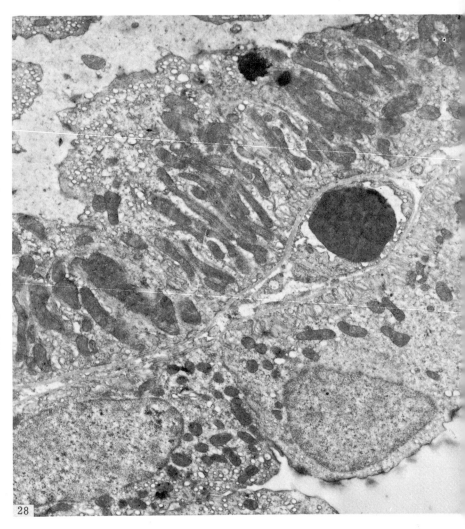

FIG. 28. *Elongated mitochondria in kidney convoluted tubule cell are shown. The large circular dark object is an erythrocyte lying within a capillary vessel. (Preparation by M. Sheridan. Photograph by R. Quinton Cox, Dept. of Anatomy, Emory Univ.)*

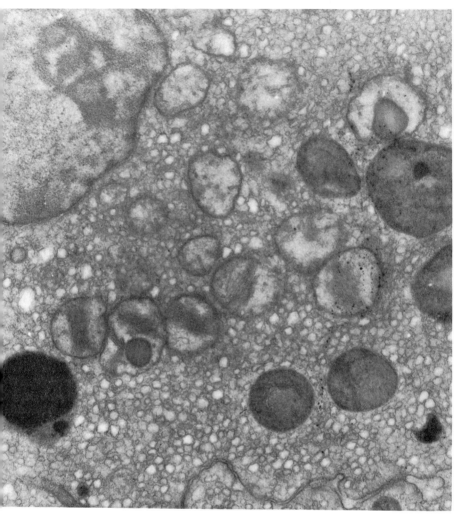

Fig. 29. *Mitochondria in adrenal cortical cell (zona fasciculata) of a guinea pig. Note cristae aggregated in bands. Portion of nucleus in top left corner. What appear to be lipid droplets are in two of the mitochondria. Other structures may be modified mitochondria. (Preparation and photograph by R. Quinton Cox, Dept. of Anatomy, Emory Univ.)*

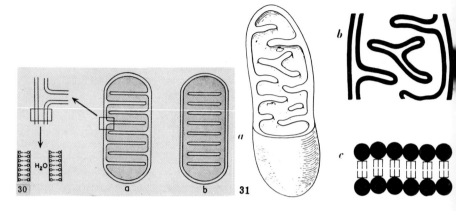

Fig. 30. *Structure of mitochondria. The figures (a) and (b) indicate the pattern of organization of mitochondria. (a) Represents the viewpoint of Palade and (b) that of Sjöstrand. The rectangle indicated in (a) is enlarged to show details of membrane structure. The probable molecular structure of each of these membranes is indicated below. The gap between the membranes is probably highly hydrated. (Legend and figure from Lehninger, Scientific American, 202, No. 5, 102, 1960.)*

Fig. 31. *Three dimensional view of structure of mitochondria which appears as a bag filled with fluid (a). The double membrane nature of the wall is demonstrated in b and the suggested molecular structure of the membranes in c. According to Lehninger each half of the double membrane consists of a single layer of protein molecules (black spheres) lined on the inside by a layer of fat or lipid molecules (prongs) directed toward each other, i.e., each of the black lines in C is composed of one layer of protein and one layer of lipid or fat. (From Lehninger, Scientific American, 1960, 202, No. 5, 102).*

Fig. 32. *Possible origin of mitochondria by infolding of cell membrane according to Robertson. "Structure and Function of Sub-Cellular Components," Cambridge Univ. Press, 1959.)*

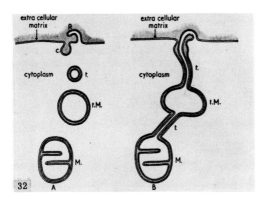

has suggested that it is possible that the mitochondria may have originated by an invagination of the membrane which was nipped off to form the mitochondrion (see Fig. 32). This is an interesting suggestion but it is not readily acceptable to most cytologists and is, in fact, considered unlikely by many of them. The membranes of the mitochondria appear to consist of two protein layers separated by a double layer of lipids. This is again characteristic of cell membrane structure.

Bensley in 1934 was the first one to isolate mitochondria by differential centrifugation, and he was able to demonstrate that mitochondria contained a considerable amount of protein, lipid, and fat. Bensley's chemical composition of mitochondria is

Proteins and unknowns	65%	Lecithin and cephalin	4%
Glycerides	29%	Cholesterol	2%

Subsequent studies have shown up to 30% of phospholipid (lecithin and cephalin). Mitochondria undergo a very considerable change under various conditions. Bensley claimed that mitochondria (as demonstrated by standard staining reactions) were greatly reduced in liver cells of starved animals, but Sheridan in our laboratory and Fawcett have demonstrated by electron-microscope techniques a great increase of mitochondria in starvation. Sheridan has further demonstrated a still further increase of mitochondria in the liver cells of guinea pigs suffering from scurvy. Mitochondria are also affected in number and form by narcotics, enzyme poisons, old age, and so on. Sometimes mitochondria store unusual compounds and sometimes they store compounds which are usual but to an abnormal degree. The double membrane enclosing the mitochondria is of a semipermeable nature and as a result of this mitochondria have been described as osmometers. There is no doubt that molecules of various sizes pass with different degrees of readiness through the mitochondrial membrane. It has been shown that large molecules pass through fairly easily while some small molecules pass through either not at all or only with very great difficulty. It has even been said by Emmelot and Bos (1956) that this permeability, particularly of liver mitochondrial membranes, is affected by thyroxine. Also there are claims by some authors that mitochondrial membranes have pores. Mitochondria may accumulate water and swell. They may do this in starvation and in various pathological conditions. When this occurs they produce the condition which the pathologists describe as cloudy swelling. Cloudy swelling has been known to occur sometimes in neoplasms and sometimes after poisoning with various toxins. The mechanics of cloudy swelling are that the mitochondria become very large and lose their cristae, the matrix stains less strongly, and sometimes the outer membranes of the mitochondria may disappear and the mitochondria may fuse and so form structures known as chondriospheres. Under some pathological conditions mitochondria may become disrupted, undergo lysis, and portions may be ejected from the cell.

Mitochondria are capable of abnormal storage. Accumulation of ferritin by mitochondria was demonstrated by Kuff and Dalton in 1957, and they may also accumulate iron pigments or bile pigments. Brachet has described ferritin particles in young erythroblasts where he says they penetrate the mitochondria and then break into smaller iron-containing particles. When the mitochondria eventually burst, the granules become scattered throughout the cytoplasm and take part in the formation of hemoglobin. Silver granules and keratinous materials have been also seen inside mitochondria. They have been found to contain melanin, and Graffi in a series of papers from 1939 to 1941 claims that they also contain or store carcinogenetic hydrocarbons. Sometimes this storage affects the function of the mitochondria, and sometimes the accumulation of material is due to malfunction of the organelle. They may also store neutral fats or lipids. In plants mitochondria have been recorded as storing starch. As a result of storage mitochondria undergo physical changes. The membrane may become single and the cristae decrease in size and may be lost altogether. If the stored substance is eliminated, the mitochondria resume their normal appearance. There is a vast literature on the role of mitochondria in the production of almost any kind of product—protein, yolk, fat, glycogen, and so on—but this is not the place to review this work. For further information see Bourne, Mitochondria and Golgi Complex in "Cytology and Cell Physiology" (2nd ed.), Oxford University Press, 1951, or 3rd ed. (to be published by Academic Press).

There have been many scornful remarks in the literature about the supposed synthetic activity of mitochondria, but the study of the enzymic equipment of mitochondria shows that they have the equipment to effect a wide range of synthetic activities.

It has been mentioned that the isolation of mitochondria by the differential centrifugation of homogenized cells was first carried out in 1935 by Bensley and by Hoerr. It was not until 10 or 15 years later that this technique became used extensively and this time by biochemists who set to work to find out the metabolic composition of mitochondria, i.e., the nature and content of enzymes concerned with metabolic processes.

THE CHEMICAL NATURE OF MITOCHONDRIA

In Bensley's work it was suspected that mitochondria contained a good deal of lipid material. One finding which suggested this was that mitochondria were stained by a method which is similar to that used for staining *Mycobacterium tuberculosis* and *Mycobacterium leprae*. These bacteria are stained by treating them for some minutes with a hot phenolic solution of basic fuchsine and once stained in this way they resist the de-staining effects of acid alcohol. This is the origin of their designation as acid-fast bacteria, and their staining idiosyncrasies are believed to be due to a waxy or lipoidal coat. Mitochondria stained by hot acid fuchsine resist the decoloring action of picric acid for longer periods than most other cell constituents, and this suggests that the mitochondria might also have a membrane which contains material of a lipoidal nature or at any rate which is of similar composition to that of the bacteria mentioned.

Mitochondria are difficult to demonstrate with conventional methods of staining if the fixative has contained acetic acid, alcohol, ether, chloroform, acetone, or other fat solvents. Also mitochondria have been found to stain with osmic acid, and, incidentally, to resist de-staining by extraction with turpentine—a property of certain types of lipoprotein complexes. Baker has found that his "acid-haematin" test for lipids applied to a variety of tissues, nearly always gave a positive, reaction with the mitochondria. Thus there had accumulated for some years direct and indirect evidence that mitochondria contained appreciable amounts of lipid. Bensley's experiments, which, incidentally, were carried out some years before Baker's staining studies, showed that mitochondria which had been produced by homogenization and differential centrifugation contained appreciable amounts of lipid (30%).

METABOLIC SUBSTANCES FOUND IN MITOCHONDRIA

Perhaps we should give a brief summary of what was suspected about the metabolic significance of these organelles prior to the revolutionary studies which were made with isolated mitochondria beginning during the middle of the 1940's. One of the characteristic staining reactions of these organelles is that they give a green or green-blue stain with Janus green B which is diethylsafranine azodimethylaniline, and it has been claimed by Cowdry that this reaction is primarily due to the diethylsafranine monocarboxylic acid component since this compound gives a very good and specific reaction with these structures. It was observed many years ago by T. B. Roberston that if one drop of a saturated solution of safranine was added to a solution of trypsin, a colored precipitate was formed, and subsequently it was demonstrated that this colored precipitate had proteolytic activity. Then Marston demonstrated that other azo dyestuffs would react in a similar way, particularly neutral red which is a dimethyldiaminotoluazine hydrochloride. Marston suggested that these results indicated that the reaction of mitochondria with Janus green might signify that they contained proteolytic enzymes. Now, the concept of the staining reaction with Janus green has been pretty well proved by Lazarow and Cooperstein to indicate that mitochondria play an important part in cellular oxidations and that the production of a pink color from the Janus green by the mitochondria is due to the DPN specific dehydrogenases. The fact that Janus green B does not stain the mitochondria permanently green but that the green color gradually becomes reduced to the pink and then to the colorless form has been known for many years.

Joyet-Lavergne demonstrated more than twenty years ago that mitochondria contain an oxidase system which oxidizes cobaltous to cobaltic salts and that these latter stain the mitochondria green. It was noted by Gatenby that in the snail, *Lymnaea,* the mitochondria are colored yellow in the natural state presumably by a carotenoid pigment; also extracted lipomitochondria frequently have a yellow appearance which too is probably due to carotene. It is of interest in this connection that it has been demonstrated by the present author and by Joyet-Lavergne that mitochondria give a blue reaction with antimony trichloride in chloroform solution, an acknowledged reaction for vitamin

A. Carotene is also a provitamin A, so these histochemical results indicate the presence of vitamin A in mitochondria. Criticism of Joyet-Lavergne's results was made by Gomori because the former author had used alcohol as a fixative. The present author has, however, always applied antimony trichloride in chloroform solution direct to fresh unfixed tissues and this suggests that this result is a true one, in any case biochemical tests have now confirmed (see Goerner) that mitochondria (prepared by homogenization and differential centrifugation of the cells) contain 27–32% of their weight of lipids and that 100 mg. of this lipid contains approximately 249–910 U.S.P. units of vitamin A. Joyet-Lavergne has suggested that mitochondria contain a redox system in which vitamin A plays a part.

A number of authors, Leblond, the present author, and Giroud and his co-workers have demonstrated that mitochondria of some organs react with acetic acid–silver nitrate solution (which has been demonstrated as being a specific reagent for vitamin C) to give a positive reaction, and this indicates that vitamin C may be present in them. One has to accept the intracellular localization of vitamin C with a certain amount of discretion in view of the very destructive effect of this reagent on the cell cytoplasm. Electron-microscope studies in the present author's laboratory have demonstrated that this reagent has a most drastic effect on the ultrastructure of the cell, and we cannot be sure that the localization of vitamin C in the mitochondria is, in fact, a real thing. It is of interest, however, that Chayen has found that the mitochondria of plant cells give this reaction very intensely and very specifically. It may be that mitochondria in plant cells and some animal cells do, in fact, contain vitamin C, but we need further studies before this can be confirmed. Other vitamins appear to be present in mitochondria, members of the vitamin B complex have been found to be present, in some cases, in the form of coenzymes. The actual vitamins of the B complex recorded are vitamin B_1 (thiamine), riboflavin, nicotinic acid (niacin), pantothenic acid, and pyridoxine. However, although these vitamins are present in mitochondria, they are not present in any greater concentration than in the other parts of the cell so that they are not exclusively contained in these organelles. These studies were made on cell homogenates and, of course, it is possible that the presence of the vitamins in the other fractions of the homogenate may be due to the fact that they have been leached out of the mitochondria by the saline solution which is used in the homogenization process in these particular experiments, and further work would have to be done before we could be certain about this.

The present author, Joyet-Lavergne, and Giroud have demonstrated that mitochondria contain glutathione or protein-bound SH, and this is further evidence that mitochondria can play an important part in oxidation–reduction mechanisms in the cell. It is of interest that mitochondria have been found in large quantities in the phloem cells of plants which are concerned with transport and may be concerned with this process. This suggestion is made in view of Conway's views that redox systems can play an important part in ion pumping. Another substance which was demonstrated histochemically in mitochondria by the present author, using the Schultz reaction, was cholesterol. This was particularly evident in the mitochondria of cells of the adrenal cortex. Similar but less intense reaction was shown by the mitochondria of the liver, and it has been demonstrated that isolated liver mitochondria contain about 2% cholesterol and it is possible they contain more in the adrenal cortex.

Bensley has recorded the presence of a red pigment in the mitochondria and also in the submicroscopic particles of the liver cell. He believed that this pigment is derived from the oxidation of unsaturated fats and possibly the phospholipids of the mitochondria, and this led him to suggest that in the liver cell the mitochondria in particular are, possibly, the seat of highly active oxidative processes which involve the metabolism of fats. The possible relation of mitochondria to oxidation–reduction processes was indicated by the publications of Ludford. He demonstrated that, if methylene blue was added to tissue cultures, the mitochondria of the cells stained a brilliant blue color but this could be inhibited by potassium cyanide. If the cells were exposed to a bright light, the blue color was rapidly bleached.

It is of interest that the mitochondria, although they have been demonstrated to contain a good deal of fat and lipid, do not give a positive reaction with Sudan III. They contain protein (quite a high proportion of it), but it is of interest that the earlier workers, using Millon's reagent, produced a negative reaction for protein. Subsequently Bensley and Gersh using a Millon's reagent of a different formula were able to obtain positive results from the mitochondria of many tissues, and they found that they were particularly well stained in frozen, dried sections and particularly in those of *Amblystoma* liver. The same authors demonstrated that, in undenatured, frozen, dried sections of *Amblystoma* liver, the mitochondria were destroyed if the sections were exposed to artificial gastric juice and artificial pancreatic juice.

Despite all this chemical information most of which was in existence by the beginning of the 1940's, there was no certainty as to the function of mitochondria, and it was not until 1946 and 1947 that the late George Hogeboom and his colleagues at Bethesda completely revolutionized our ideas of their function by demonstrating that the major proportion of the succinic dehydrogenase and an appreciable proportion of the cytochrome oxidase activity of the liver cell were present in the mitochondria. This at once suggested that these organelles were the major sites of aerobic respiration in the cell. It is of interest that as long ago as 1915, Dr. Kingsbury had suggested that mitochondria were concerned with the respiration of the cell. His reasons for this were largely due to his observations that anesthetics such as ether and chloroform, which depressed cellular respiration and the respiration of the animal in general, also broke up mitochondria in the cell. The work of Hogeboom and his colleagues was carried out on homogenates of liver which had been produced by grinding up liver with saline. This gave poor preservation of the form of the mitochondria and subsequently 0.8 M sucrose was used—this preserved the nature and form of the mitochondria very well. In the beginning there was some doubt as to whether the material being assayed was in fact mitochondria or not, but when sucrose was used this doubt gradually disappeared. Eventually electron-microscope studies of the structure of the granules isolated by homogenization and differential centrifugation demonstrated beyond doubt that they contained the same structures as the mitochondria of normal cells. Another possible source of error, however, began to haunt the biochemists and was frequently verbalized by cytologists and this was that the mitochondria did not really contain the oxidative enzymes, mentioned in the foregoing, but that they were being absorbed or adsorbed by them from the homogenate. This possibility was negated at least in part by adding more enzyme to the homogenate and demonstrating that it could be recovered almost 100% from the supernatant and so was not taken up by the mitochondria. Thus the localization of the enzymes in the original cell was probably in the mitochondria (see Fig. 33).

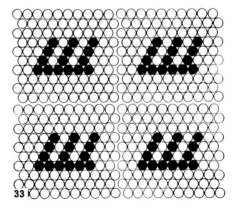

FIG. 33. *Localization of respiratory chain enzymes (black spheres) in the mitochondrial membrane. Since they are proteins they form part of the protein layer. According to Lehninger they are arranged in groups distributed at regular intervals in the protein layers of the membrane. (From Lehninger, Scientific American, 1960, 202, No. 5, 102.)*

33

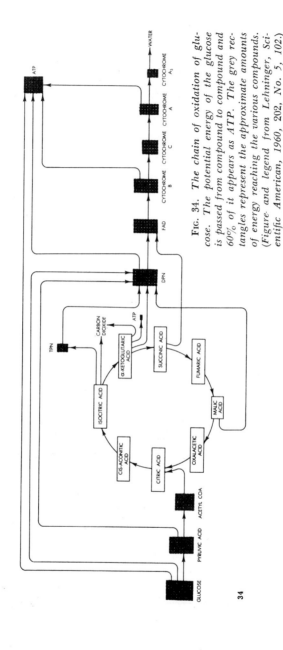

FIG. 34. *The chain of oxidation of glucose. The potential energy of the glucose is passed from compound to compound and 60% of it appears as ATP. The grey rectangles represent the approximate amounts of energy reaching the various compounds. (Figure and legend from Lehninger, Scientific American, 1960, 202, No. 5, 102.)*

34

Subsequently, Kennedy and Lehninger demonstrated that in addition to containing cytochrome oxidase and succinic dehydrogenase, mitochondria also catalyze the condensation of pyruvic acid with oxaloacetic acid, the formation of succinic acid from α-ketoglutaric acid, and the formation of malate from succinate. These three reactions represent three steps of fundamental importance in the Krebs tricarboxylic acid cycle of which we will have more details shortly. Mitochondria also contain coenzyme I of which nicotinamide is an important constituent and cytochrome reductase which is a flavoprotein. These two enzymes are links between the Krebs tricarboxylic acid cycle and the cytochrome system, and it, therefore, appears that mitochondria probably contain the whole enzymic equipment necessary for aerobic respiration of the cell. In fact, it was originally demonstrated that a centrifugate of cells which included only nuclei and mitochondria were capable of carrying through the whole of the oxidation of glycogen to CO_2 and water; subsequently it was demonstrated that isolated mitochondria on their own could do this (see Fig. 34). Transaminase activity was subsequently demonstrated in mitochondria although in only the same concentration as in the rest of the cytoplasm. Transaminase is concerned with protein synthesis and it is of interest that pyruvic, oxaloacetic, and α-ketoglutaric acids are the corresponding α-keto acids of the amino acids, alanine, aspartic and glutamic and need only to be transaminated to produce them. Since the former compounds are themselves formed as intermediates in the course of the Krebs cycle, this indicates a mechanism whereby mitochondria might synthesize fresh protein material and so increase in size themselves or synthesize protein for other parts of the cell. This possibility is further extended by the fact that RNA is known to be present in varying amounts in mitochondria, although the exact amount is uncertain and there is a possibility of contamination of mitochondria with RNA from the rest of the homogenate when making such estimates. However, there is no doubt that mitochondria do have the equipment for synthesising protein although to what extent they do this *in vivo* is not known. (See Horning's illustration, Fig. 35, of apparent formation of protein by mitochondria in "Opalina.") All the fatty acid oxidase activity in the cell is also in the mitochondria and so is 80% of the octanoxidase activity. Since these discoveries, an enormous amount of work has been done on the mitochondrial enzymes and this work was summarized by Hogeboom (unfortunately now deceased), Kuff, and Schneider from the National Institutes of Health and has been published in Volume 6 of *The International Review of Cytology*, 1957. It may be of interest to record here other enzymes and compounds which they listed as being present in mitochondria (see Table I).

Fig. 35. *Apparent synthetic activity by mitochondria (Mt) in the protozoan* Opalina. *It is suggested by Horning and Richardson that the material produced is protein.* (Arch. Exp. Zellforsch., 1929, **10**, 488.)

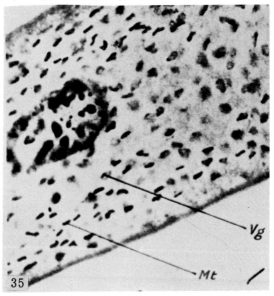

TABLE I

Enzymes in Mitochondria

Enzyme or Compound	Per cent activity
Isocitric dehydrogenase (TPN linked)	58.4
Aconitase	85.7
Fumarase	67.2 (rabbit cerebral cortex)
Fumarase	54.6 (mouse liver)
Cytochrome c	48.3
Acetyl CoA deacylase	7.1 (but in plants it is largely present in the mitochondria)
Cysteine desulfhydrase	4.8
Xanthine dehydrogenase	nil
Choline esterase	21.5 (rat liver)
Histaminase	0.4
Arylsulfatase	6.0
Alkaline phosphatase (phosphomonoesterase)	8–17
Acid phosphatase	55.0
Ribonuclease	54.0
Nucleoside phosphotransferase	49.0
Choline oxidase	—[a]
Choline dehydrogenase	—[a]
Betaine dehydrogenase	—[a]
DPN oxidase	—[a]
Acetate activating enzyme	—[a]
Unsaturated fatty acyl cohydrase	—[a]

[a] Specific figures not available.

It is of interest too, that a considerable amount of ribonuclease and deoxyribonuclease are present in mitochondria—this seems unusual since only a very small amount of DNA and a relatively small amount of RNA are present in the mitochondria compared with other parts of the cell. However, it is possible that the bodies which contain RNAase and DNAase are not true mitochondria but are lysosomes; we will discuss these shortly. In the meantime, it is of interest to note that it was eventually demonstrated by fragmenting mitochondria and separating the membranes from the contents that cytochrome oxidase and succinic dehydrogenase activity were located primarily in the membranes (see Fig. 33). Subsequently it has been shown that the ability of the mitochondria to carry out the Krebs cycle and to combine this with oxidative phosphorylation is dependent on the presence of intact double membranes in the mitochondria. Now, it has been demonstrated and mentioned earlier that in the structure of mitochondria there is an outer membrane and an inner membrane to the mitochondrion, so that it is surrounded by a double membrane. Also, the inner membrane is folded inward to give elongated cristae, and these cristae, because they consist of a fold of the inner membrane, are themselves double membranes. There appears to be little difference biochemically between the double membrane structures of the cristae and the double membrane structure of the outer wall of the mitochondria.

An important factor in the process of oxidative phosphorylation is the transport of electrons. Dr. David E. Green has described the process of electron transport as carried out fundamentally with the aid of an electron transport particle—this is a submitochondrial particle. The latter can be isolated in a form so that it can no longer carry out the full citric acid cycle, but it can still carry out the process of oxidative phosphorylation which it performs by the oxidation of succinate and DPNH (reduced diphosphopyridine nucleotide, a codehydrogenase) with the aid of the cytochrome system. When mitochondria are freshly prepared by homogenization and differential centrifugation and are then exposed to alternate freezing and thawing, their form undergoes considerable change. First of all, the external membrane ruptures and some of the cristae break off, and eventually the mitochondrion is completely disintegrated; however, fragments of double membrane structure are left which, according to D. E. Green, may be derived either from the cristae or from the outer envelope of the original mitochondrion. These double membrane fragments represent collections of Dr. Green's electron transport particles.

(Figures 36–39 demonstrate the appearance, under the electron microscope of different types of mitochondrion.)

If other methods are used for preparing these particles and the particles so produced do not show a double membrane structure, then oxidation of succinate and DPNH coupled with phosphorylation does not occur. Apparently the double membrane structure is essential for this process to take place. In the structures which do not have the double membrane structure, the capacity for electron transport is still present but oxidation phosphorylation cannot take place.

About 35% of the dry weight of the electron transport particle of Green is composed of lipid, and the lipid is concentrated in packets of lipoprotein. These are interspersed between two molecules of cytochrome or between a flavoprotein and cytochrome. In other words, all the oxidation reduction members of the electron transfer chain are connected to one another by lipoproteins. These lipoproteins, according to Green, act not only as structural devices, holding various enzymes together, but they also contain a compound which can shuttle electrons back and forth so that they can pass from cytochrome through to flavoprotein and reverse. This compound, which Green and his colleagues have described, is a new coenzyme called coenzyme Q. It is a completely water insoluble benzoquinone derivative, which is concentrated in the lipoproteins of the electron transport particles and is related to vitamin K. Coenzyme Q can undergo oxidation and reduction in a similar fashion to cytochromes; for instance, the quinone part of the molecule can be reduced to become a hydroquinone and the hydroquinone can be reoxidized. It is pretty certain that this coenzyme plays an important part in the electron transfer chain of the particle. The significance of the electron transport in these mitochondrial membranes may seem obscure but, as Green points out, one should think of this problem of electron transport in terms of its coupling—the fact that the process can be coupled to the esterification of inorganic phosphate. In this process a monophosphoric ester of the hydroquinone or, what Green described as a semiquinone form of coenzyme Q would be formed. This ester would then react with adenosine diphosphate by a process of transphosphorylation and ATP would be formed, and simultaneously the semiquinone or hydroquinone would be oxidized to the quinone form in coenzyme Q by the ferric form of cytochrome c. The production of ATP is, in fact, the reason for the existence of such a system. This explanation of the way in which the oxidative processes of the mitochondria actually are used to produce ATP by oxidative phosphorylation is an extremely fundamental discovery, and Green and his co-workers are to be complimented very much on the extraordinary patience and care which they have put in over a large number of years to work out this very complex problem in mitochondrial physiology.

In view of the studies by Green and his colleagues which have just been described, it is of interest to consider some of the studies of Martias. This author has for some time put forward the view (1954) that there may exist in mitochondria two routes for the transport of hydrogen ions or electrons, respectively, between the pyridine nucleotides (DPN and TPN) and cytochrome c. He thought that only one of these would be linked with enzymes which brought about phosphorylation. The route which is best known leads from DPN to cytochrome c reductase and then to

FIG. 36. *Collection of cytoplasmic bodies in cell from adrenal cortex near junction of zona fasciculata and zona reticularis. A large myelin-like structure is seen at the top of the illustration enclosing what is probably a drop of lipid. Immediately below it is a mitochondrion with bands of cristae typical of a zona fasciculata cell. Black bodies are possibly lipid although the one in the lowest part of the micrograph appears to have mitochondrial-like cristae. Near it is a typical mitochondrion with conventional cristae. (Preparation and photograph by R. Quinton Cox, Dept. of Anatomy, Emory Univ.)*

FIG. 37. *Cell from zona reticularis of guinea-pig adrenal cortex. Nucleus on left. A number of mitochondria containing lipidlike bodies are seen. Portions of the membranes of some of the mitochondria appear imperfect. (Preparation and photograph by R. Quinton Cox, Dept. of Anatomy, Emory Univ.)*

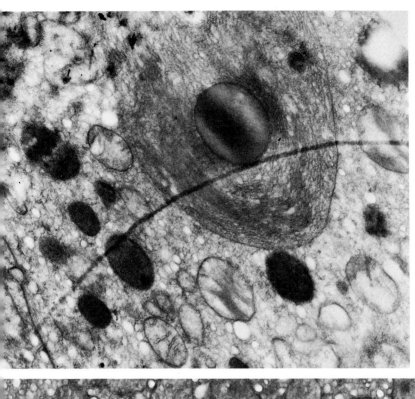

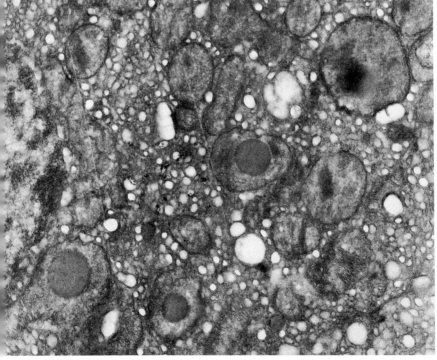

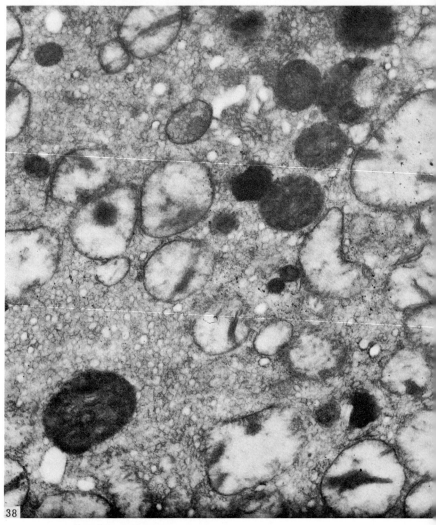

38

FIG. 38. *Cell from zona fasciculata of guinea-pig adrenal cortex. Many typical mitochondria are seen. There are also a number of bodies containing small spherical multilaminate myelinlike bodies. Are these aberrant or modified mitochondria? Note many mitochondria show imperfections in their membranes. (Preparation and photograph by R. Quinton Cox, Dept. of Anatomy, Emory Univ.)*

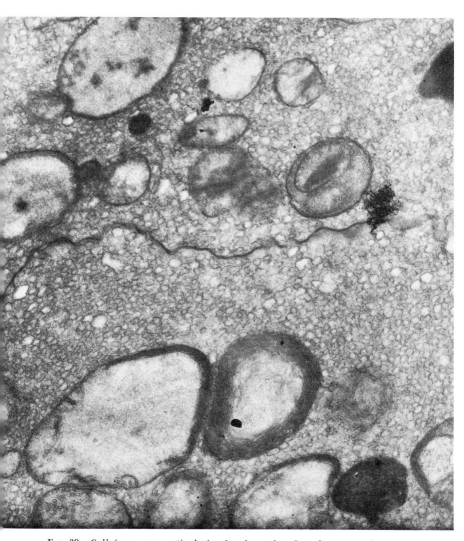

Fig. 39. *Cell from zona reticularis of guinea-pig adrenal cortex. A malformed mitochondrion is seen on the right. At the bottom of the micrograph various stages showing the origin of myelin bodies from mitochondria are shown. Whether these bodies are just aberrations or whether they have some special significance in cell physiology is not known. Defects in membranes of some mitochondria are seen and in both lower and upper halves of the micrograph aggregations of mitochondrial cristae without a peripheral membrane can be seen. (Preparation and photograph by R. Quinton Cox, Dept. of Anatomy, Emory Univ.)*

cytochrome c. Martias believes that this particular route is not one which is concerned with the formation of high-energy phosphates. On the other hand, he proposed a second alternative route in which vitamin K (phylloquinone) is an important factor. Until recently this concept of an electron transport system involving vitamin K in mitochondria has not proved to be particularly popular, Martias and Strouff have finally isolated a phylloquinone reductase that is a flavoprotein having a number of similarities to cytochrome c reductase. There is, however, a difference between them. Phylloquinone reductase and cytochrome c reductase can both react in the reduced state with phylloquinone, but with cytochrome c only cytochrome c reductase will have any effect. Vitamin K reductase has an extremely high activity even in relatively low concentrations.

If we consider that there are two routes in mitochondria which can be used for electron transport, then the problem to be solved is what decides whether these electrons and hydrogen atoms are directed into either of these particular pathways. Under normal circumstances they seem to be directed exclusively along the pathway which is coupled with oxidative phosphorylation and which leads via vitamin K reductase to vitamin K, cytochrome b and so through to cytochrome c.

This pathway via vitamin K seems to be sensitive to any alteration of the internal structure of the mitochondria, possibly because some of its constituents, particularly the vitamin K, are associated with the double membranes of the cristae. If their combination is disturbed, the electrons take the emergency route which is via cytochrome c reductase to cytochrome c. It is of interest in connection with this theory that dicoumarol is capable of decoupling oxidative phosphorylation from respiration, and, since dicoumarol is known to be a vitamin K antagonist, its action is possibly explicable by the fact that it blocks the pathway between vitamin K and its reductase. It is also of interest that thyroxine is a hormone which causes uncoupling of respiration from oxidative phosphorylation. Since it is known that, if thyroxine is added to mitochondria, it causes a swelling and change in the internal structure, this would be perhaps further evidence that the internal structure of the mitochondria is the one which is particularly concerned with the flow of electrons along the route leading to oxidative phosphorylation. It may well be that hormones which affect respiration do so by affecting the structural nature of the mitochondria, apart from their effects on the endoplasmic reticulum which have already been mentioned. The precise relation between Green's coenzyme Q and Martias' vitamin K phylloquinone reductase is not absolutely clear, but it is very likely they are identical or closely related systems.

LYSOSOMES

De Duve in his studies on ultracentrifugation of cytoplasmic particles has demonstrated that some particles appear to contain acid phosphatase, cathepsin, and β-glucuronidase and ribonuclease, DNAase and cholinesterase. It is of interest that these compounds appear to be present in separate particles—they require higher centrifugal forces for sedimentation than do the cytochrome-oxidase bearing mitochondria. De Duve has pointed out that it is of special interest that such hydrolytic enzymes are in special particulate bodies differing from others of the cytoplasm. He is not clear as to how this should be interpreted but has pointed out that, if hydrolytic enzymes are free to act within the living cell, as, for instance, they can do in homogenates, they would interfere with the efficiency of the synthesis and may even affect the structural integrity of the cell; he then suggests that segregation of hydrolytic enzymes in this way is one method by means of which this activity is either kept in check or localized in specific parts of the cell. De Duve once described these bodies as "suicide bags" and suggested that on the death of the cell these enzymes are released completely into the cytoplasm and play a part in the process

of autolysis. The present author has suggested that these
enzymes may be less effectively contained in the lysosomes
in senescence and that this leakage may be partly responsible for the cellular process of aging. It is of interest that
lysosomes have been demonstrated *in situ* with the electron
microscope and stained to demonstrate their acid phosphatase activity. No typical mitochondrial structure can be
seen in these bodies and they appear to be of a different
nature from mitochondria.

THE METABOLISM OF CARBOHYDRATES

The role of mitochondria in oxidative phosphorylation
has already been mentioned and their role in the metabolism
of carbohydrates through the presence in their substance of
enzymes concerned with the Krebs cycle and the cytochrome
system has been indicated. We should now consider the
problem of carbohydrate metabolism and the role that
mitochondria and other parts of the cytoplasm play in it.

Carbohydrate metabolism is extremely important for cell
synthesis and is the main source of energy for cell activities.
Before attempting to localize the various activities of carbohydrate metabolism in the actual parts of the cell, we should
consider briefly what the metabolism of carbohydrates involves. There are two types of metabolism, anaerobic and
aerobic. The anaerobic route is demonstrated very well by
muscle, and most of the information on this type of metabolism of carbohydrates has been obtained by studies of this
tissue.

The result of anaerobic metabolism is the production of
lactic acid and the liberation of a good deal of CO_2. However, although we think in terms of anaerobic metabolism
for muscle, we have to realize that muscle itself has a first
class blood supply which appears to be increased by various
physiological mechanisms when muscle is forced to do work
and that muscle in the process of contraction uses a rather
surprisingly large amount of oxygen.

Lactic acid has been shown to accumulate in muscle
extracts and in isolated muscles kept under anaerobic con-

ditions. If we consider the accumulation of lactic acid in an animal *in vivo,* we find that after moderate work the accumulation of lactic acid goes up slightly but remains at a pretty steady level. However, if strenuous work is done, then the amount of lactic acid goes up extremely steeply and slowly comes back to normal. The reason for this is that under normal circumstances muscle can obtain oxygen fast enough to reoxidize the lactic acid as rapidly as it is formed and only a small amount of lactic acid accumulates. However, it is possible for muscle to do more work than it can supply oxygen for and it can do this by oxidizing carbohydrates anaerobically and so accumulating lactic acid. Eventually this lactic acid has to be converted with the aid of oxygen but this can take place over a longer period. Some of the lactic acid is converted into glycogen in the liver and the rest is oxidized. The fact that it is possible to accumulate lactic acid and slowly oxidize this after the work is finished provides a mechanism by means of which an "oxygen debt" can be produced. Under aerobic circumstances it is not lactic acid which is formed in the metabolism of carbohydrates but pyruvate. However, this does not accumulate and it is oxidized almost as rapidly as it is formed—as we shall see in a minute there is a very complicated system for oxidizing this pyruvate. The only time when pyruvic acid does accumulate in the tissues is in the absence of vitamin B_1 or thiamine, a fact which was demonstrated years ago in Oxford by R. A. Peters. Under anaerobic conditions pyruvic acid undergoes the process known as oxidative decarboxylation with the aid of the cocarboxylase (thiamine pyrophosphate). It yields acetate, carbon dioxide, and lactate. It has been stressed that this reaction is fundamentally of an oxidative nature and leads to the term oxidative decarboxylation which is an important process both in carbohydrate and protein metabolism.

We have mentioned the production of pyruvate but have not yet considered the process by means of which this compound is produced—this process is known as glycolysis and it represents the first stage in the metabolism of carbohydrates. Glycolysis is, in effect, the reverse of photosynthesis. In photosynthesis the energy of sunlight is used to combine CO_2 and water into carbohydrates; in the process of glycolysis, the glucose which is formed from carbohydrates such as glycogen and other polysaccharides is converted into CO_2 and water with the liberation of energy. We can express this as $C_6H_{12}O_6 + 6\ O_2 = H_2O + 6\ CO_2 +$ energy. This oxidation of glucose to give CO_2, water, and energy is not a single step but involves a very large number of steps of considerable complexity. During the various steps, small packets of energy are released at a rate at which the cell can use them, whereas if there was a sudden explosive release of energy by the oxidation of glucose the cell would probably not be able to use this relatively large amount of energy in a coordinated way and a good deal of it would probably be wasted.

The first stages of glycolysis involve the phosphorylation of glucose and this is done with the aid of ATP as follows (the enzyme concerned in this process is placed above the arrow):

$$\text{glucose} + \text{ATP} \xrightarrow{\text{hexokinase}} \text{glucose-6-phosphate} + \text{ADP}$$

Hexokinase is not just one enzyme, there are in fact a number of hexokinases that catalyze phosphorylation of hexoses. The phosphorylation of glucose results in the transferring of a high-energy phosphate from the ATP to glucose and so to form a phosphate ester which is poor in energy—this type of reaction is called an exergonic reaction and is essentially irreversible. It is of interest that one of the properties of glucose-6-phosphate which differs from glucose is the fact that the phosphate ester has difficulty in penetrating cell membranes whereas glucose itself, apparently, crosses without any difficulty, and it has been suggested that this hexokinase reaction is one way in which glucose can be locked in a cell. It is also an essential prerequisite for the resynthesis of glycogen.

Many things can happen to glucose apart from phosphorylation and ultimate conversion into CO_2 and water via the glycolytic and Krebs cycle system. Amongst these are its dehydrogenation by a glucose dehydrogenase to form gluconic acid. This is done by a diphosphopyridine nucleotide (DPN) linked (codehydrogenase) reaction. In mammals, it is believed that this is not a usual pathway for glucose to follow. If glucose can be locked into position in a cell by being converted into a phosphate, it is obvious that there must be in existence a mechanism which can release it again since it needs, for instance, to be fed from the liver periodically into the blood stream to keep the blood glucose level at a relatively constant figure. This is carried out by a specific enzyme, glucose-6-phosphatase,

$$\text{glucose-6-phosphate} + H_2O \xrightarrow{\text{G-6-Pase}} \text{glucose} + PO_4.$$

This glucose-6-phosphatase is probably present in all tissues which release glucose from cells, but it does not appear to occur in skeletal muscle.

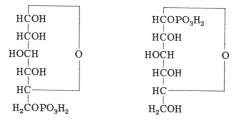

Glucose-6-phosphate   α-Glucose-1-phosphate

Glucose-6-phosphate may be converted into glucose-1-phosphate, in other words the phosphate is simply shifted around from the 6-position to the 1-position on the glucose molecule. This change of position of the phosphate group is catalyzed by an enzyme known as phosphoglucomutase, and the reaction changing the phosphate group from one part of the molecule to the other is an easily reversible reaction. The formation of glucose-1-phosphate from glucose-6-phosphate is a stage in the synthesis of glycogen, for instance, if glucose is accumulating in a cell it is converted to glucose-6-phosphate and then to glucose-1-phosphate. The

molecule of glucose-1-phosphate then polymerizes into glycogen. The reverse process can occur—glucose-6-phosphate
can be obtained from glycogen by first producing glucose-1-
phosphate and then by producing glucose-6-phosphate from
the glucose-1-phosphate. We have, however, diverted a little
from the direct line of our story of the glycolytic cycle. After
the formation of glucose-6-phosphate from glucose, the next
stage in the glycolytic cycle is the conversion of glucose-6-
phosphate into fructose-6-phosphate. This reaction is readily
reversible and is catalyzed by an enzyme called phospho-
hexose isomerase.

Fructose-6-phosphate may also be formed directly from
fructose, and it is known that an enzyme, fructokinase, which
is present in brain and muscle can produce this effect. The
next step is the further phosphorylation of fructose-6-phos-
phate; another phosphate group is added in the 1-position
to give fructose 1-6-diphosphate. The enzyme responsible
for this is phosphofructokinase and the reaction is carried
out with the aid of ATP:

$$\text{fructose-6-phosphate} + \text{ATP} \xrightarrow{\text{PFkinase}} \text{fructose-1-6-diP} + \text{ADP}$$

This reaction is also exergonic.

Fructose-1-6-diphosphate is also known as hexose diphosphate and in the next stage this is broken down by what is
described as the "aldolase" reaction into 3 phosphorylated
compounds—triosephosphates. The first of these is ketose
triosephosphate, the second is dihydroxyacetone phosphate,
the third is phosphoglyceraldehyde. The triosephosphate
can be converted into phosphoglyceric acid; dihydroxyacetone phosphate can be converted into phosphoglyceraldehyde or alternatively it can be reduced to α-glycerophosphate
with the aid of DPNH and α-glycerophosphate dehydrogenase. This reaction is potentially important for the
synthesis of lipids since from the α-glycerophosphate, phosphatidic acid can be synthesized, and phosphatidic acid can
be the starting point for the synthesis of lecithin, cephalin,
and also of fats. Phosphoglyceric acid with the aid of the

enzyme enolase becomes converted into phosphoenol-pyruvic acid.

Pyruvic acid penetrates cell membranes very well and can thus leave the cell and in theory can be distributed in any cell in the body.

Conversely all the steps which we have mentioned can be reversed and pyruvate can be converted back into glucose-6-phosphate. When pyruvic acid is reduced it gives lactic acid. Lactic acid itself can be converted back to pyruvic acid. Liver cells are capable of reversing the whole glycolytic series of reactions and can produce glucose and glycogen again from lactic acid. Muscle can reverse lactic acid to glucose-6-phosphate and glucose-1-phosphate and glycogen but cannot produce nonphosphorylated glucose.

In these first stages of carbohydrate metabolism, a certain amount of energy is liberated but this is not much more than about one-tenth of the total amount of energy which is produced by the production of CO_2 and water from glucose. The glycolytic part of the cycle is the least energy producing part. In addition to its conversion into lactic acid or its oxidation, pyruvic acid can be converted to alanine, an amino acid, by the process of transamination. Thus here one can see a link between carbohydrate and protein metabolism.

If there is ample oxygen, the pyruvic acid produced by this first stage of carbohydrate metabolism can be oxidized. This is a complex process in which in the first stage the pyruvic acid is converted by the process of oxidative decarboxylation into acetyl coenzyme A and CO_2. Thiamine pyrophosphate (cocarboxylase) is an essential enzyme for this process.

Acetyl coenzyme A is a 2-carbon substance and it condenses with oxaloacetic acid which is a 4-carbon dicarboxylic acid to yield a 6-carbon tricarboxylic acid, namely, citric acid. The enzyme catalyzing this is called the "condensing enzyme." Thus starts a series of changes which ultimately lead to the formation of CO_2 and water. The production of citric acid is followed by the loss and recapture of water, and it becomes converted to *cis*-aconitic acid (with the aid of aconitase, glutathione, and ferrous iron) which on further hydration is converted into isocitric acid. This compound then loses hydrogen and thereby becomes oxidized to oxalosuccinic acid (this reaction is catalyzed by isocitric dehydrogenase) and decarboxylation turns it into α-ketoglutaric acid (the enzyme responsible is oxalosuccinic decarboxylase and oxidized manganese). α-Ketoglutaric acid is decarboxylated and then oxidized by the loss of two hydrogen atoms to succinic acid (the enzyme concerned is α-ketoglutaric dehydrogenase). Succinic acid is also oxidized by the loss of H_2 (with the help of succinic dehydrogenase) to fumaric acid. The latter by the addition of the elements of water becomes converted by fumarase into malic acid, and the malic acid by dehydrogenation (enzyme malic dehydrogenase) is converted in oxaloacetic acid, and there we are back at the beginning of the cycle again. The oxaloacetic acid is ready to combine with another molecule of acetyl coenzyme A to produce citric acid once more. During this process 3 molecules of CO_2 are given off and 5 molecules of H_2.

It can be seen that quite a complex series of reactions take place in what has been called the "tricarboxylic" or "citric acid cycle," or the "Krebs cycle." All three terms are applicable.

The final combination of the hydrogen atoms liberated by the Krebs cycle with oxygen is brought about by the cytochrome system. It is of interest that cytochrome is a protein which contains a form of heme, an iron containing pigment which is also present in hemoglobin. It is probably more widely distributed than any other type of heme protein since it occurs in the cells of all organisms that use oxygen, irrespective of whether they are animals or plants or whether in the case of animals they are vertebrates or invertebrates, or protozoa.

In the cytochrome system a variety of compounds and enzymes are involved. Cytochrome oxidase is a widely distributed enzyme since its occurrence is comparable in distribution to cytochrome. It has not yet been obtained pure, and it has been found to be bound to the insoluble material when cells are homogenized and spun down. This is not surprising when we appreciate that cytochrome oxidase is associated with the mitochondria. There is also another compound involved called flavoadenine dinucleotide (FAD for short) which is associated with various proteins to form a variety of different enzymes. A flavine containing enzyme was first isolated and called a yellow ferment as long ago as 1932 by Warburg and Christian. Flavoproteins are usually associated with metals of various sorts, and molybdenum, copper, and iron are three which have been found to be necessary for their adequate functioning. It is not quite clear where the metal atoms are situated on the molecule but they appear to be essential for the action of the enzymes with which they are associated. There are two types of riboflavin containing enzymes, one type is an electron acceptor from reduced DPN or TPN, and it can transfer these either to oxygen or to the cytochromes, whereas the other type of flavoprotein accepts electrons directly from metabolites. Among the important flavoproteins is cytochrome reductase which comes in two types—one for reduced DPN (DPNH) and the other for reduced TPN (TPNH). The oxidation of these two compounds (DPNH and TPNH) in the cell can thus be carried out by the cytochrome system.

Now we are in a position to describe the next stages which take place in the oxidation of glucose. The 5 pairs of hydrogen atoms which are passed down to the cytochrome system from the Krebs cycle are combined with the cytochrome and result in its reduction. The enzyme concerned is cytochrome reductase, the flavoprotein already mentioned. Cytochrome is then oxidized with the aid of cytochrome oxidase, which removes the hydrogen atoms. They become combined with atmospheric oxygen to produce water and thus the long journey of oxidation of carbohydrates is done, 5 molecules of water and 3 molecules of CO_2 being produced from each molecule of pyruvate. Although the course may seem tedious and involved to the reader of the preceding pages, all these reactions take place in a flash.

An analysis of oxygen uptakes of various tissues in the body gives an indication of the degree to which their cells are metabolizing. As a matter of interest, it might be noted that of the tissues examined, retina and kidney had the highest metabolism and liver was next, then the rate decreased progressively from adrenal, lung, bone marrow, diaphragm, heart, lymph nodes, skeletal muscle, skin to eye lens which had the lowest level of oxygen consumption. The important point to remember is that the complex of reactions described above is localized to a great extent in the mitochondria.

One of the important functions of this oxidative cycle just described is its relationship to phosphorylation. We have described earlier the work of Green who showed that oxidative phosphorylation could take place without the whole Krebs cycle occurring, but in intact mitochondria the whole cycle normally goes through and phosphorylation is an important by-product of these reactions. This process of phosphorylation results in the production of high-energy phosphate esters, such as ATP.

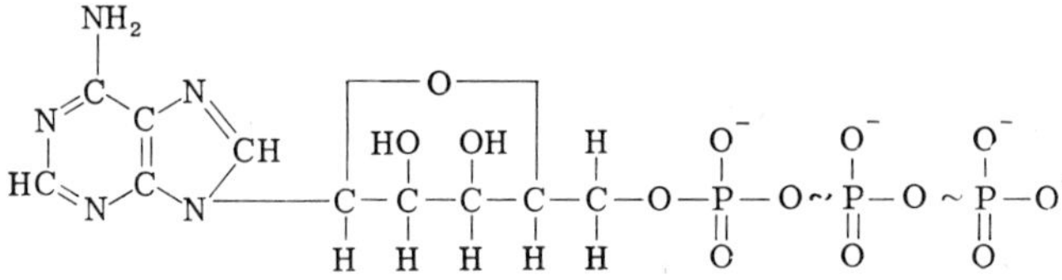

Adenosine triphosphate (ATP)

Since ATP is one of the principal energy containing compounds of the body, it is very important in the whole energy cycle of the cell. It is, for example, the main source of energy in muscular contraction and for many of the

FIG. 40 *(right). Aldolase preparation of intestine showing diffuse reaction in the smooth muscle. (From Allen and Bourne, J. Exp. Biol., 1943, 20, 61.)*

synthetic processes of other cells. (See Fig. 33 for a summary of these processes.)

This briefly is the story of carbohydrate metabolism in the cell. What we want to try to do now is to demonstrate where this complex of activity is situated in the living cell. It appears that most of the processes of respiration and glycolysis actually take place in the cytoplasm and mitochondria. Some years ago (1941), the present author and R. J. Allen demonstrated that zymohexase which is really a complex of two enzymes and is concerned with the splitting of hexose diphosphate (the aldolase reaction) was localized in the cytoplasm of the cell and in the case of muscle fibers in between the fibrils in the sarcoplasmic material rather than in any of the formed elements. It is noted too that the results of differential centrifugation of cell homogenates have demonstrated that most of the enzymes responsible for the glycolytic cycle have been found to be present either in the supernatant or in "microsomes" and those concerned with the cytochrome system and Krebs cycle are localized specifically in the mitochondria. Now, since the microsomes mostly represent fragments of the endoplasmic reticulum,

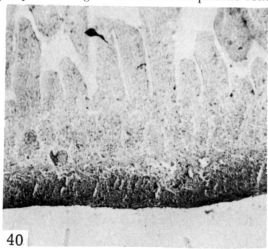

40

we can assume that most of the enzymes found in them can also be found in the membranes of the endoplasmic reticulum. In addition to the aldolase complex (see Fig. 40) which has been demonstrated to be present in the supernatant, it has been found that phosphorylase and phosphoglucomutase and glucose-6-phosphate dehydrogenase have also been found in the supernatant and glycolysis has in fact been found to take place in this fluid—a fact which confirms that all the glycolytic enzymes necessary for this process must be present there. However, glucose-6-phosphatase has been found not to be localized at all in the supernatant but exclusively in the microsomes (fragmented endoplasmic reticulum). There is some evidence too that hexokinase is present in the microsomes. On the other hand, DPNH and DPN and TPN-linked cytochrome c reductases which are found in high concentration in mitochondria have also been found to be present in the microsomes. It might be possible to suggest from these facts a tentative scheme which would help us to understand to some extent the relationship between the reactions occurring in the cytoplasm itself and those in the mitochondria.

Let us assume that glucose passes across the cell membrane, perhaps it is taken in by pinocytosis as has been suggested by a number of authors or, possibly, if and when the membranes of the reticulum are continuous with the outside of the cell, it may simply pass up the cisternae between the membranes of the reticulum and enter into the cell through the membranes of this reticulum. Let us assume that the glucose has passed into the cell by the process of pinocytosis. Then, with hexokinase present in the cytoplasm, it can be converted into glucose-6-phosphate and subsequently run through the cycle to pyruvate. At this point (another system which we will discuss in a minute) associated with the mitochondria comes into play. If the glucose has to pass across the cell membrane or across the membranes of the endoplasmic reticulum, it should also be able to do this without too much difficulty. If any glucose-6-phospate should occur in the cisternae it will probably be able to pass freely into the cytoplasm because of the presence of glucose-6-phosphatase in the membrane. It may be that there is hexokinase in the fluid within the cisternae and that, perhaps, all the glucose there (if any) is first phosphorylated and then released in a timed fashion into the cytoplasm through the action of glucose-6-phosphatase in the membranes. Perhaps this is a way of controlling the feeding of the carbohydrate fuel into the furnace. It will be remembered that glucose-6-phosphate passes cell membranes with difficulty unless there is the appropriate hydrolytic enzyme on the membrane. The glucose, once into the cytoplasm by whatever route, can be synthesized into glycogen or it can be brought to pyruvate by the enzymes of the glycolytic cycle which are known to occur in the cytoplasm. Once pyruvate is prepared, it is changed into acetyl coenzyme A and is ready for the next stage. For this it has to come into contact with the mitochondrial membrane. Whether it has to pass through the mitochondrial membrane and come in contact with the cristae we do not know, but the existing evidence suggests that the envelope and cristae of mitochondria have fundamentally the same enzymatic structure. Furthermore, there are pores and even large openings in some mitochondrial envelopes and there is thus little difficulty in metabolites passing in or out. Now, it has been mentioned that a great proportion of the enzymes concerned with the Krebs tricarboxylic acid cycle are localized in the mitochondrial membranes and since acetyl coenzyme A appears to be the most commonly used fuel of this system, it is at this point that the mitochondria largely take over the final oxidative stages. Thus, as far as we can tell at the moment either in the cytoplasm of the cell itself or in the endoplasmic reticulum, glycolysis occurs with the production of either acetyl coenzyme A or pyruvic acid. We do not know at what stage the latter are fed to the mitochondria. They must go largely to the mitochondria because these organelles contain the greatest proportion of the Krebs cycle enzymes—it is these latter which complete the oxidative breakdown of carbohydrate that was set into motion by hexokinase. The rate of penetration of these fuels into, or their absorption onto the mitochondria will be conditioned both by the nature of the mitochondria and the total area of mitochondria available. If under normal conditions we have a large number of mitochondria occupying the cell, we can assume, other things being equal, that oxidation should be proceeding at a fast rate. However, where one gets a large increase of number of mitochondria as, for example, in starvation this may be compensatory hypertrophy and not indicative of increase in oxidative activity. We do not know whether the nature of the mitochondrial surface varies from time to time but we know that the surface area varies. Mitochondria, for instance, fragment from the filamentous and rodlike condition to the granular state under a variety of circumstances. These include mechanical damage to the cells, rough handling, influence of bacteria and other toxins, as a result of anesthesia and anoxia, and so on. It can be shown mathematically that there is a greater surface area available the more fragmented the mitochondria become. Because of this either the pyruvate and/or acetyl coenzyme A can feed more rapidly into or become attached in larger amounts to the mitochondria when they are in a fragmented condition simply because there is a greater surface area. Thus the mitochondria in virtue of their ability to fragment and reform into the filamentous condition can act as a throttle controlling the rate of aerobic metabolism in the cell. They may also have an additional means of doing this, a sort of fine control. Since it is fairly certain that enzyme molecules are aligned along the cristae, these structures represent another surface where reactions can take place, and reduction in the size and number of cristae would also have a throttling effect on the metabolism or synthesis due to mitochondria. This can be seen in operation in the case of a mitochondrion which has accumulated a good deal of fat or other product of chemical reactions. In such a case, the cristae are reduced or absent altogether as if metabolic processes are brought to a virtual standstill because of the accumulation of reaction products. This brings us to another process of control, a chemical method known as "feedback" which will be discussed shortly.

Siekewitz believes that both glycogen synthesis and breakdown take place at the surface between the cytoplasm and the ergastoplasmic membranes in association with the enzymes present at those surfaces. He points out, however, that only glucose-6-phosphatase and DPNH and TPNH cytochrome c reductases (these latter are believed to act as coenzymes for glycolysis in the early stages of glucose oxidation) have been found to be associated with the microsome fraction, but he believes that the site of effective action of the other enzymes might be at the interface between the membranes and the matrix of the cytoplasm. He suggests that hexokinase might be activated at the membrane surface of the endoplasmic reticulum. Other cofactors such as glucose-1-6-diphosphate and adenosine monophosphate possibly also bind their appropriate enzymes to the E.R. membranes.

Siekewitz has also discussed certain biochemical aspects of the control of glucose metabolism.

First of all he points out that, if the concentration of glucose in the lumen of the endoplasmic reticulum is in equilibrium with the glucose concentration in the blood (this assumes at least temporary continuity between the lumen or cisternae of the E.R. and the exterior of the cell), there exists then a mechanism whereby the glucose level in the blood would definitely affect intracellular glucose equilibrium. Thus a reduced production of glucose from the diet would lead to reduction of glucose in the blood and this would cause a reduction of the amount of glucose in the fluid within the endoplasmic reticulum. The latter result would lead to increased phosphatase activity which would cause an increase in the breakdown of glycogen (e.g., in the liver cells) and a production of glucose which would pass out from the endoplasmic reticulum into the blood stream.

Siekewitz points out that hexokinase, phosphoglucomutase, and phosphorylase might have their activity enhanced if they were attached to the endoplasmic reticulum membranes. In the case of phosphorylase, active phosphorylase B has to undergo a conversion to active phosphorylase A before it can have any catalytic effect. An enzyme phosphorylase B-kinase carries out this conversion by phosphorylating the enzyme in the presence of ATP. Siekewitz suggests that this kinase may be part of the membrane of the endoplasmic reticulum and that the activating process for phosphatase in the cell might consist of moving it out of the cytoplasm onto the site of the E.R. membranes. Siekewitz points out that it is possible that hormones control this type of movement of enzymes within the cell and its internal membranes. At this point one might remember the work quoted earlier by Brandes and the present author in which it was demonstrated that shifts of acid phosphatase activity took place from the Golgi apparatus to the nucleus in ventral-lobe prostate cells following castration and that acid phosphatase activity was restored to the Golgi apparatus following implantation of the male sex hormone. Also of interest are the further studies of Brandes in which he has demonstrated that in castrated animals there is a rearrangement of the membranes of the endoplasmic reticulum. These studies demonstrate a definite morphologicobiochemical effect on the part of the male sex hormone. Siekewitz suggests that the hormones concerned with carbohydrate

Fig. 41. *Schematic representation of relationship of endoplasmic reticulum to carbohydrate metabolism. (From Siekewitz, "Regulation of Cell Metabolism," Ciba Foundation Symposium, 1959, Churchill, London.)*

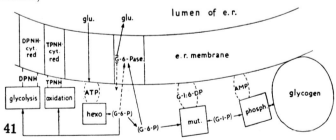

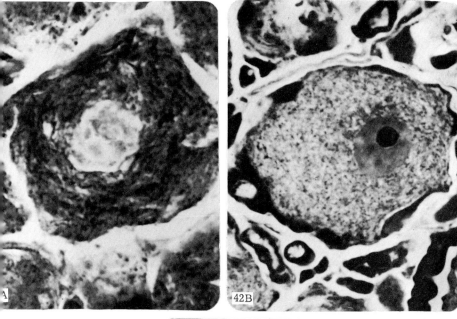

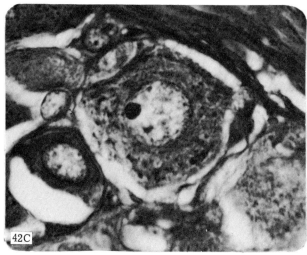

Fig. 42 *A, B, and C. A. Apparent localization of 5-nucleotidase on the endoplasmic reticulum of spinal ganglion neurons. B and C. In other metabolic stages of the spinal ganglion cells, the enzyme is seen to be localized in cytoplasmic granules and in the nucleolus. (Preparation and photograph by H. B. Tewari, Dept. of Anatomy, Emory Univ.)*

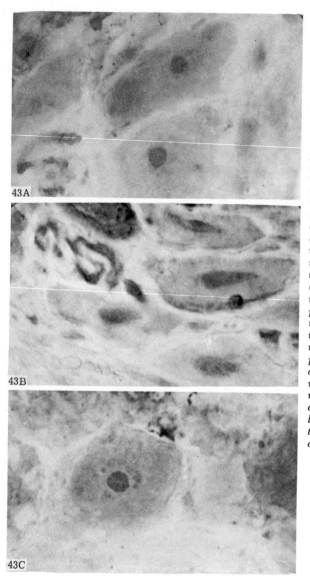

43A

43B

43C

Fig. 43. Glucose-6-phosphatase in rat spinal ganglion neurons. (A) Note reaction restricted to nucleolus; (B) note reaction in nucleus, nucleolus still positive appears outside the nucleus and in contact with the cell membrane; (C) strong reaction in nucleolus, rest of nucleus and cytoplasm give moderate diffuse reaction; (D) moderate reaction in nucleus, stronger in cytoplasm, intense perinuclear reaction; (E) nucleolus and nucleus slight to negative reaction, reaction in cytoplasm appears to be associated with the endoplasmic reticulum; (F) completely negative nucleus and nucleolus. Cytoplasm filled with large negative vacuoles; cytoplasm between the vacuoles is strongly positive.

These results suggest a cyclic metabolic activity in the spinal ganglion cells. It is possible that glucose-6-phosphatase is synthesized in the nucleolus and passed first to the nucleus and then to the cytoplasm where it becomes associated with the endoplasmic reticulum. The presence of large synthetic products in the cytoplasm suggest the participation of the glucose-6-phosphatase in some synthetic process. This product is not glycogen, but some of our protein and fat preparations show moderate sized droplets which could be identical with the vacuoles. (Preparations and photographs by H. B. Tewari, Dept. of Anatomy, Emory Univ.)

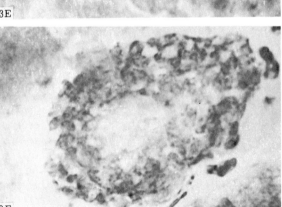

43D

43E

43F

metabolism do not act directly on the enzyme as such but bring it and the substrate and various cofactors together at a suitable surface and then complex them together there. (See Fig. 41.)

Other enzymes may be localized on the endoplasmic reticulum e.g. 5 nucleotidase (see Fig. 42).

The nucleus, as will be described later, appears to be enclosed in a fold of the double membrane of the endoplasmic reticulum and not to have a membrane of its own. Since the E.R. spaces might be connected directly to the exterior of the cell, it is possible that glucose coming from outside the cell could be converted into glucose-6-phosphate in the E.R. lumen and thus be prevented from passing through the E.R. membrane. Thus it could pass along all the ramifications of the E.R. canals and come in direct contact with the nuclear fold of the reticulum. If this membrane contains glucose-6-phosphatase (and a number of our histochemical studies suggest that it does, see Fig. 43), it could penetrate through into the nucleus without having to pass through the cytoplasm at all. Histochemical preparations show that the glucose-6-phosphatase reaction in a particular histological section is not always positive for all nuclei in the section, and it is of interest that Siekewitz has pointed out that enzymes may be present or activated at the E.R. membrane only when the glucose concentration reaches a critical level.

It is of interest that histochemical studies of the cells of many organs demonstrate the fact that many dephosphorylating enzymes as well as glucose-6-phosphatase show an association with nuclear membranes—perhaps here lies the mechanism whereby even low levels of glucose-6-phosphate could penetrate readily through into the interior of the nucleus. The endoplasmic reticulum could provide a pathway straight to the nucleus which would prevent glucose from getting in contact with or passing through the cytoplasm where it could be attacked by glycolytic enzymes. This may be the mechanism by which a supply of glucose to the nucleus is ensured. Glucose could also be supplied to the nucleus from the cytoplasm by the process of glycolysis. In this case, glucose being formed from glycogen as glucose-6-phosphate would be dephosphorylated and pass through the E.R. membrane and into the lumen where possibly it would be rephosphorylated to prevent its passing back again and would thus move along the lumen to the nucleus. Hence the nucleus could get its glucose directly from the cytoplasm via the endoplasmic reticulum or directly from the outside (the latter, however, only if a direct connection really exists).

In many cells the mitochondria can also be seen to be completely surrounded by endoplasmic reticulum. It is possible that the mitochondria themselves obtain their glycolytic fuel directly as a result of glucose passing through the E.R. membranes undergoing glycolysis there and the glycolytic products feeding directly to the mitochondria.

The control of the rate of different types of metabolism, particularly respiration, in the cell can depend on two main factors. First, a structural factor which brings into apposition the appropriate reactants and which varies with the extent of the surfaces available for these processes to take place, and, second, it may also depend on some chemical feedback where an excessive production of one kind of compound inhibits its continued production or slows down further synthesis. Alternatively, the metabolism in any one particular direction may be affected by the absence of a limiting amount of some specific substance or compound in the reaction chain.

Sir Hans Krebs in a recent article entitled "Rate Limiting Factors in Cell Respiration" discussed the control of energy utilization and pointed out that, in unicellular organisms, energy can be obtained directly from oxidation if air is present but if air is not present then anaerobic fermentation takes its place and energy is obtained by this source. In this instance it is the supply of air or oxygen which regulates which of these mechanisms comes into use, and oxygen is, in fact, the "rate limiting factor." In higher animals the ability to undergo fermentation or an aerobic oxidation is still present and can be particularly well demonstrated in muscle. Krebs pointed out that the chemical systems in the cell which are concerned with the function of regulation are all fairly simple reactions but that there is an elaborate interlocking of these reactions. By this he means that the individual reactants may take part not only in more than one reaction but in very many different processes. One of the difficulties in sorting out such a complex of activity is that not all the component reactions of this elaborate interlocking series are known and we are dealing with a heterogeneous system in which there are many varied membranes and different spatial arrangements of the various reactants. He also points out that regulation is probably a matter of reaction velocities, some of which will be accelerated and some slowed down and the question that has to be decided is the degree to which any of these are rate-limiting. Krebs illustrates this point by considering the amount of oxygen used by 4-ml. sheep heart homogenate, which contained about 10% of tissue (see tabulation).

Substrate added	O_2 (μ mole) used by 4 ml suspension
None	17
Pyruvate	26.1
Succinate	32.6
1-Lactate	21.6
Citrate	20.8
α-Oxyglutarate	25.4
Fumarate	19.1
Acetate	21.1
Glycogen	15.4

Thus one can demonstrate that the addition of glycogen adds nothing to the oxygen uptake so the amount of glycogen present is not a limiting factor in this system. The same applies if glucose is added instead of glycogen. On the other hand, when acetate, pyruvate, or other intermediates of the tricarboxylic acid cycle are added there is an appreciable increase in the rate of oxygen uptake. The fact that the oxygen uptake in this system can be increased if suitable substrates are added to the mixture demonstrates that the electron transport system from DPNH to oxygen is not being used to its full capacity, thus it cannot be the factor which is limiting the uptake of oxygen. Certain special substrates which are known to reduce either DPN or flavoprotein seem to be able to increase oxygen consumption. Thus the limiting factor appears to be that, the mechanism for the transport of hydrogen from DPN or flavoprotein is not being used to its full capacity if these special substrates are not present. The limiting step therefore is really the first stage in the electron transport system. If it is found that a particular substrate increases the rate of respiration this is due to the fact that the substrate reacts more readily or easily with DPN or flavoprotein than any endogenous substrate already present. This is the reason why pyruvate or α-ketoglutarate or succinate are responsible for the stimulation of respiratory rate in the experiment quoted. However, even if we accept this we are still faced with the identification of the factor that decides the rate of reaction between substrate and DPN or flavoprotein.

Studies with dinitrophenol which decouples oxidative phosphorylation from respiration is of interest and helps to throw light on this problem.

Perhaps we should first say a word or two about this action of dinitrophenol. The uncoupling of oxidative phosphorylation from respiration has been compared to putting a car into neutral gear and still leaving the engine running. If the respiratory activities are regarded as the engine and the phosphorylation as the process of making the car go, then dinitrophenol uncouples the engine from the transmission of the car, the engine continues to turn but the car does not move; in the cell the respiration goes on quite happily but no ATP is formed. Normally ATP is formed from ADP and inorganic phosphate and thus the factor which limits the rate of oxygen consumption and oxidation of pyruvate in the normal system such as we have described is not really the amount of enzymes present but actually the level of either ADP or inorganic phosphate. In the experiments carried out by Krebs, inorganic phosphate was present in a fairly good concentration and further quantities added to the system did not stimulate respiration. Therefore it is almost certain that the limiting factor must be the amount of ADP which is available. These experiments demonstrate the type of chemical control which a single compound can exert on a whole chain of reactions. One should also remember that another mechanism, a structural one that controls the rate of respiration, is the rate at which glucose can enter the cell and this can be hormonally controlled, although the method of action of the hormone is not exactly known. It is of interest that one of the factors which probably affects the rate at which glucose can enter the cell (if, in fact, the endoplasmic reticulum is continuous with the outside of the cell) is the degree of complexity of the endoplasmic reticulum. If this structure develops many ramifications, as presumably it seems able to do in certain cells such as spermatocytes, as demonstrated by Fawcett, then the surface area available for glucose to enter into the cytoplasm of the cell and so be metabolized is enormously increased or, conversely, it may be decreased by a reduction in complexity of the reticulum.

To return to the subject of respiration and ATP formation, the reaction for this process can be given as follows:

$$C_6H_{12}O_6 \text{ (glucose)} + 6\ O_2 + 38\ ADP + 38\ H_3PO_4 \rightarrow$$
$$6\ CO_2 + 44\ H_2O + 38\ ATP$$

This is the general reaction and is a summary of all the complex intermediatary reactions which in the end simply produce carbon dioxide, water, and ATP. Since, as Slater and Houlsman have pointed out, cells contain only relatively small amounts of ADP, as soon as it is all converted into ATP the process of respiration will stop—ADP is thus the limiting factor. However, when the cell is stimulated to do work there is a breakdown of ATP according to the formula given by Slater and Houlsman,

$$38 \text{ ATP} + 38 \text{ H}_2\text{O} \rightarrow 38 \text{ ADP} + 38 \text{ H}_3\text{PO}_4 \rightarrow \text{work}$$

and, since ADP is now being re-formed, respiration can go on so long as there is some left to be resynthesized into ATP. The addition of further ATP will, of course, keep respiration going.

It is of interest that, if mitochondria that have been separated from the cell by differential centrifugation are permitted to stand for some hours at room temperature, the phenomenon of uncoupling (which can also be brought about by dinitrophenol) of the oxidative phosphorolytic system from respiration takes place. This type of mitochondrial preparation is described as "aging" mitochondria, and it is tempting to speculate whether in senescing tissues there may not be a progressive uncoupling of respiration from oxidative phosphorylation or a progressive hydrolysis of ADP so that less and less of this becomes available for synthesis of ATP. It has been possible to isolate from mitochondria which have been aged in this way, a heme compound which will actually produce this uncoupling reaction. It has been described and given the name "mitochrome" and is fundamentally a pigment. However, there appears to be a lipid component in this "mitochrome" heme-protein preparation which is the actual factor responsible for uncoupling, and the heme protein of the mitochrome is not, in fact, the uncoupling factor at all. Mitochrome is very similar in structure and form to cytochrome and is probably derived from it. Certain unsaturated fatty acids such as oleic acid are also found to be active as uncoupling agents, and the lipid isolated from the mitochrome particle also appears to contain an unsaturated fatty acid. The fact that an uncoupling agent can be produced *in vitro* this way is of considerable importance since it seems possible that the formation of such a substance in mitochondria might take place *in vivo* and may itself function as a controlling agent for respiration and oxidation.

The general view of metabolism of fatty acids at present is that they are broken down beginning at the end of the chain where the carboxyl group is, and then the chain is progressively degraded as two carbon pieces are removed by a process of oxidation. This type of oxidation of fatty acids is known as β-oxidation and is so called because the fatty acid is attacked oxidatively at the β-carbon atom in the first instance. Among the products of this oxidation is the formation of acetyl coenzyme A and acyl coenzyme A. The latter can be subjected to further oxidation with the production of more acetyl coenzyme A (CoA). Although very little has been said about the mechanism of degradation of all these fatty acids, it is of interest that the enzymes which catalyze these reactions are all located in or on the mitochondria. The acetyl CoA can enter the Krebs cycle by condensing with oxaloacetic acid and the final oxidation thus follows the same path as the carbohydrates. The acetyl CoA formed from pyruvic acid (i.e., from carbohydrate breakdown) can be used to synthesize fats and likewise so can acetyl CoA produced as a result of protein metabolism. We see, therefore the reason why the Krebs tricarboxylic acid cycle has been spoken of as the meeting place of protein, fat, and carbohydrate metabolism.

Where precisely in the mitochondria the enzymes responsible for β-oxidation of fatty acids are centered is not known for certain. It is very likely that they are more associated with the outer membrane of the mitochondrion than with the cristae so that the problem of penetration of the fatty acid through the membrane of the mitochondrion does not become so important. On the other hand, there is some evidence that pores occur in the mitochondrial membrane and if this is the case it is possible for the long-chain fatty acids to pass into the interior of the mitochondria and to become subject to β-oxidation at this site by enzymes located in the cristae. Hoberman has shown that in the mitochondria, deuterium labeled DPNH, which has been reduced during the oxidation of fat in the organelles, is not available for reactions that take place in the outside cytoplasm. This suggests that the enzymes concerned with the oxidation are localized within the cristae. It is of interest that recent electron micrographs of the adrenal cortex have shown large areas of the surface where the mitochondrial membrane is incomplete, and the interior of the organelle is thus open to the penetration of the largest molecules and even particles of fat. Novikoff's scheme for the differential distribution of biochemical activities in liver cells is shown in Fig. 44.

Fat is metabolized largely in the way already described, but the synthesis of fat is also an important part of the activity of the cell. Fat cells have an important mechanical function to perform and fat itself is a valuable reserve store of energy. Fats, fatty acids, and phosphorylated fats (phospholipids such as lecithin) are also important structural units of cell, mitochondrial, and other membranes, and their synthesis becomes an important cellular activity. Fatty acids are made up of long chains of carbon atoms, usually an even number, with a COOH group stuck at one end. Fat is formed from a fatty acid molecule by a combination between the latter and a molecule of alcohol such as glycerol. The link takes place through the COOH group which reacts with the OH of the alcohol to eliminate a molecule of water. Fatty acids may be short or long or intermediate chained, a typical short-chain fatty acid is acetic acid which has only 2 carbon atoms, and a typical long-chain fatty acid is palmitic acid which has 16 carbon atoms. (See Fig. 45.)

In the synthesis of these long-chain fatty acids, the starting point appears to be acetic acid. This combines with CoA to form acetyl CoA. This condenses with CO_2 to form malonyl CoA (the coenzyme A ester of malonic acid). This

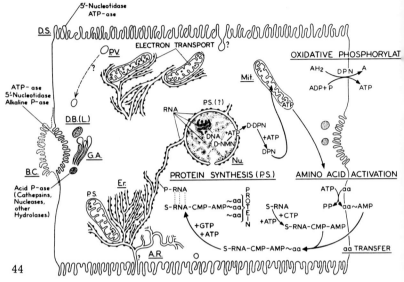

Fig. 44 (above). Differential distribution of biochemical activities in the liver cell according to Novikoff. A, oxidized substrate; aa, amino acid; AH, reduced form of substrate; ADP, adenosine diphosphate; AMP, adenosine monophosphate; AR, agranular reticulum (smooth E.R.); ATP, adenosine triphosphate; ATPase, adenosinetriphosphatase; BC, bile canaliculus; CMP, cytosine monophosphate; CTP, cytosine triphosphate; D-DPN, desamido diphosphopyridine nucleotide; DPN, diphosphopyridine nucleotide; DNA, desoxyribonucleic acid; D-NMT, deamido nicotinic acid mononucleotide; DB, peribiliary dense bodies; Er, ergastoplasm; GA, Golgi apparatus; GTP, guanosine triphosphate; L, lysosomes; Mit, mitochondria; Nu, nucleus; P, inorganic phosphate; P-ase, phosphatase; P-RNA, particle ribonucleic acid; PP, inorganic pyrophosphatase; PS, protein synthesis; PV, pinocytosis vacuoles; RNA, ribonucleic acid; S-RNA, soluble ribonucleic acid. (From Novikoff, 1960, Am. J. Med., 29, 102.)

Fig. 45 (right). Fatty acids build up from acetic acid units which are made reactive by combining first with coenzyme A to form acetyl-CoA (top) and then with carbon dioxide to form the CoA ester of malonic acid (second line). Malonyl-CoA and acetyl-CoA can condense (third line) into an intermediate compound. Further reactions not yet fully explained then reduce the intermediate to the CoA ester of a four-carbon fatty acid (fourth line). This like acetyl-Co-A can condense with a molecule of malonyl-CoA, ultimately giving the ester of the six-carbon fatty acid; the chain thus lengthens by successive steps. The molecules always join head to tail, the carboxyl head of the fatty acid joining the methyl tail of the malonyl-CoA. The letter R symbolizes the 82 atoms in coenzyme A other than sulfur. (This scheme is slightly modified from Lehninger, Scientific American, 1960, 202, 102.)

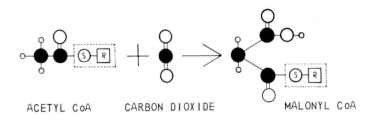

ACETIC ACID   COENZYME A   ACETYL CoA

ACETYL CoA   CARBON DIOXIDE   MALONYL CoA

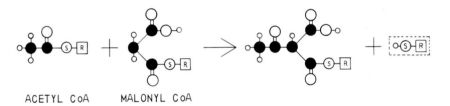

ACETYL CoA   MALONYL CoA

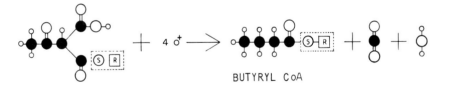

4 σ⁺

BUTYRYL CoA

○   HYDROGEN   ●   CARBON
◯   OXYGEN   Ⓝ   NITROGEN
Ⓟ   PHOSPHORUS   Ⓢ   SULFUR

latter compound then condenses with another molecule of acetyl CoA to form an intermediate substance which becomes reduced to form a 4-carbon fatty acid which condenses with a molecule of malonyl CoA to give a 6-carbon fatty acid and so the carbon chain is built up. Then, as described, combination of the appropriate fatty acid with an alcohol such as glycerol gives an ester known as a fat.

Phospholipins such as lecithin, which play a very important part in the structure of the cell membranes, also have to be synthesized by the cell. These compounds are not only esters of a fatty acid but are simultaneously esters of phosphoric acid. In this synthetic activity ATP plays an important part. It starts the ball rolling by phosphorylating one of the OH groups of glycerol. To the other two OH groups, CoA esters of palmitic acid are attached. At this point the phosphoric acid group that was put on in the first step drops off. The molecule then reacts with a compound known as cytidine diphosophocholine. This compound, which is really a coenzyme, drops the diphosphocholine part of its molecule nicely into the spot on the OH group which had been vacated by the first phosphoric group and so the lecithin is formed.

Other coenzymes are concerned with the production of the other steps in the synthesis but these will have to be studied in more specialized works of biochemistry. Dr. D. E. Green has pointed out that one of the surprising things about the synthesis of fatty acids is that the synthesis stops at 16-carbons. It is rare to get 12- and 14-carbon chain fatty acids, and 18- or more carbon chains scarcely ever form. What tells the cell to break off the synthesis at that point is certainly an intriguing problem.

Although one would expect that mitochondria would be the principal fatty acid synthesizers of the cell, the belief at the moment is that they are not the site of synthesis and that it takes place at the surface of the endoplasmic reticulum. However, in the production of fats from the fatty acids and especially in the case of lecithin synthesis where

ATP is required, the mitochondria make a contribution to the synthesis because of their ability to produce the latter material. Mitochondria do play a direct role in fat metabolism but, this role as mentioned earlier in this chapter, appears to be in fat degradation rather than in fat synthesis.

PLANT CELLS

So far we have considered only animal cells, and it is of interest that Hackett in the International Review of Cytology (Vol. 4, 1954), has pointed out that in plant cells glycolysis involves the plastids, the soluble fraction of cells and possibly the nucleus as well as the mitochondrial enzymes. He points out that many enzymes which are involved in the Krebs cycle are not exclusive to the mitochondria and that hydrogen transfer is not confined to these organelles. Mitochondria he says react with the nucleus in the process of phosphorylation, they react with the chloroplasts in photosynthesis, and they react with the microsomes in protein synthesis in the endoplasmic reticulum. He believes that a close relation between the cell membrane and the mitochondria may play an active part in the movement of substances into the cell or possibly in the growth of the cell wall of plants. Furthermore, he reminds us that the real unit is the cell itself, its various parts work as an integrated unit, and one should only break them down for the purpose of trying to analyze the various processes in which they participate.

CHAPTER V

The Golgi apparatus

As all cytologists know, the Golgi apparatus was a structure first described in 1898 by the Italian neurologist Golgi, in the nerve cells of the Barn Owl. Since the discovery of this organelle it has been the subject of very great controversy and in the last 50 years there have been at least 2000 papers written about it. The standard technique for differentiating the Golgi apparatus has been by the use of osmium or silver salts after appropriate fixation of the cell and the most characteristic form for the organelle which has been demonstrated is that of a network. In the case of the nerve cell, this network extends pretty well through most of the cytoplasm of the cell (see Fig. 46), in other cells it is a small compact area situated to one side and closely applied to the nucleus. The conception that the Golgi apparatus existed as an osmiophilic or argentophilic network was challenged by a number of workers. Parat and his school believed that the Golgi apparatus really consisted of a series of vacuoles which stained with neutral red and an extension of this hypothesis, e.g., by John R. Baker of Oxford, conceived of the network actually being produced by the deposition of metals, osmium or silver, on the periphery of the vacuoles so that eventually a networklike structure was built up. Very complex functions were deduced for the Golgi apparatus, and it was

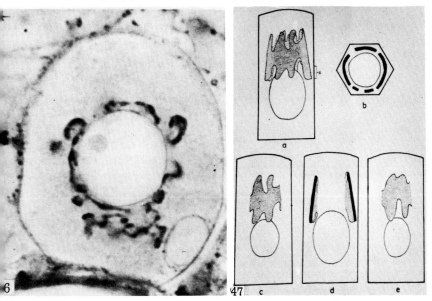

FIG. 46 *(left). The Golgi apparatus in a spinal ganglion cell. Notice its aggregation around the nuclear membrane. (Preparation and photograph by E. S. Horning, from "Cytology and Cell Physiology," 1951, Oxford Univ. Press.)*

FIG. 47 *(right). The nature of the Golgi apparatus of the epithelial cells according to Pollister. a, The whole collar in a vertical section of the epithelium; b, a cross section of the cell taken at "X." c to e, are upper, middle, and lower focal planes, respectively. (From Pollister and Pollister, 1957, Int. Review of Cytol., 6, 85.)*

believed to play a part in the formation of the acrosome of the sperm and to be concerned with yolk reproduction of the egg and secretion products in other cells, particularly those of the glandular cells.

Dr. Pollister in the International Review of Cytology (vol. 6) has discussed the structure of the Golgi apparatus (Fig. 47) and pointed out that many authors have described the apparatus as being lamellar in shape. He pictures it as being composed of irregularly circular, flattened, lamellae

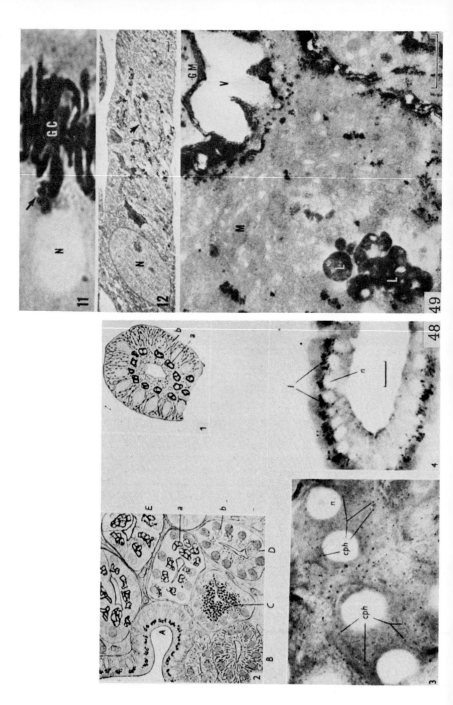

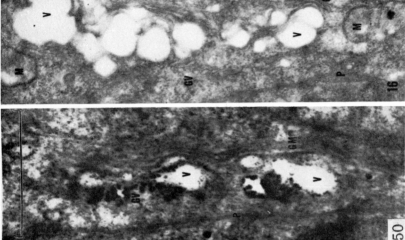

FIG. 48 (top, left). 1. Pancreatic cell, silver stain; both mitochondria and Golgi apparatus blackened by silver (from Cajal). 2. Submaxillary gland of young rabbit, silver stain; in one acinus, B, the mitochondria are blackened by silver, in another, b, the zymogen granules, and in a third, a, the Golgi apparatus (from Cajal). 3. Binuclear neurons of the coeliac ganglion of the rabbit colored with Sudan black, showing "cerephos" globules. 4. A frozen section of the intestinal epithelium of the mouse colored with Sudan black to show lipid globules in position of Golgi apparatus. (Figures and legends from Baker, "Mitochondria and other Cellular Inclusions." S.E.B. Symposia, Cambridge, 1957.

FIG. 49 (top, right). Electron microscopy of the Golgi apparatus. 11. Golgi network in epithelial cell of mouse epididymus. Lipid droplets also visible (see arrow). 12. Low-power electron micrograph of a portion of an epithelial cell from the same block as 11. The Golgi network is also blackened. 13. Higher-power electron micrograph of section from same block as 11 and 12. A group of lipid droplets is seen at the lower left, and membranes and vesicles of the Golgi complex, all containing reduced osmic acid, are present at the upper right. (Figures and legends from Dalton and Felix, "Mitochondria and other Cytoplasmic Inclusions." S.E.B. Symposia, 1957, Cambridge Univ. Press.)

FIG. 50 (right). Electron microscopy of Golgi apparatus. Left. Part of Golgi apparatus of mouse duodenal cell. Osmic acid has been reduced at the margins of the large vacuoles and within the small vesicles or granules but not in association with the membrane system. Right. Finer detail of Golgi complex of duodenal cell of mouse. (Legend and figure from Dalton and Felix, "Mitochondria and other Cytoplasmic Inclusions." S.E.B. Symposia, Cambridge Univ. Press, 1957.)

which surround one end of the nucleus. In various studies
Pollister attempted to measure the thickness of these lamellae and apparently they were in some cases thinner than 1μ
and in others around 0.25 or 0.20μ. The apparatus is capable of considerable distortion and can be seen, in fact, distorted in the contracting smooth muscle fiber but appears
to return to its normal shape once the force which is alter-
ing its shape is removed.

Possibly one of the most interesting developments of the
study of the Golgi apparatus was its isolation from the
epithelium of the epididymis of mouse and rat by Dalton
and Felix in 1954. This was obtained by differential centrifugation from homogenates. It is also of interest that the
Golgi apparatus appears to resist a good deal of damage to
the cell. As long ago as 1925, Avel showed that, if living
cells were ruptured by osmotic means, the Golgi apparatus
was often one of the last parts of the cell to undergo disin-
tegration. The Golgi apparatus was extremely difficult to
see in the living cell under the standard techniques of optical microscopy even with the phase contrast microscope;
(however, with better techniques it was visible in germ cells).

The whole controversy about the Golgi apparatus appears
to have been now reconciled by the studies with the electron
microscope. The work responsible for this was done by
Felix and Dalton as described in a series of papers published
between 1953 and 1957 and also by Sjöstrand. They
showed that the Golgi apparatus consisted of a series of
pairs of membranes adjacent to the nucleus which contained
dilatations giving the appearance of vacuoles. (See Figs. 48,
49, and 50.) This structure thus explains many of the controversial results of the early workers. Sjöstrand, who con-
tributed to the elucidation of this problem with his col-
league Hansen, has stated that the membranes which constitute the Golgi apparatus form a system (about 60 A thick).
These membranes are arranged in pairs. Along their edges
there may be points of fusion followed by dilated areas (the
vacuoles). The width of the space between the pairs of

membranes (60 A) is, apart from the presence of vacuoles, usually fairly constant. These pairs of membranes seem to be embedded in ground substance which is fairly homogeneous and has little structure, but in some cases it seems to contain fine granules or a fine reticulum. One of the characteristics of the Golgi apparatus which might otherwise have led it to be confused with the E.R. membranes is that the space between the latter, as previously described, measures 150 A. Furthermore ribonucleoprotein granules are attached to the outside of most of the E.R. membranes, but the membranes which constitute the Golgi apparatus are quite smooth and have no granules associated with them although there are reports of relatively large granules (400 A across) being situated on or near the pairs of membranes in some cases. It is interesting that this characteristic structure which has been found for the Golgi apparatus is pretty well uniform in the cells of most species of animals and in cells belonging to a wide variety of organs; for instance, gland cells, nerve cells, mucle cells, and most of the other cells in the body show the same sort of general Golgi picture.

The Golgi apparatus has been characterized throughout the literature as being that part of the cell in which the products of secretion are first recognizable microscopically, and Hirsch has even described in this living pancreatic cell small granules which were attached to the surface of the mitochondria becoming detached and moving through the cell cytoplasm toward the Golgi material.

The amount of information on the chemical nature of the Golgi apparatus is very large and very confused. We have just noted that the Golgi apparatus is composed of paired membranes which are dilated in parts to give the appearance of spheres, but this description of the Golgi apparatus does not satisfy all the various descriptions of the forms which it takes in different cells when viewed by the light microscope. The relationship of this suggested ultrastructure to, for instance, the production of oögenesis and spermatogenesis has yet to be worked out. It is of interest here to note that Dr. H. B. Tewari has recently demonstrated that in the langur monkey, *Semnopithecus,* Golgi bodies pass from the follicular cells of the ovary into the developing cocyte where they appear to play a part in the elaboration of yolk. The passing of these bodies from one cell to another is the really fascinating part of this observation.

The electron microscope will probably, in due course, give us some information on the nature of Hirsch's so-called presubstances and what relationship they bear to a fully devoloped Golgi system. The significance of the difference in the physical nature of the apparatus in different cells will need to be explained, too. For instance, in most cells the specific gravity of the Golgi apparatus is less than that of the other cellular constituents but in uterine gland cells this is not so. In the cells of these organs it seems, in fact, to be a relatively rigid structure. Pollister has suggested that the Golgi apparatus could not be a fluid or even highly plastic solid but that it has fundamentally a platelike form with enough elasticity to bend under pressure and straighten out again when the pressure was removed. Simpson, on the other hand, has claimed that it was always in a highly fluid condition. It is obvious that a good deal of the Golgi problem has to be reexamined and many light microscope studies remade in view of the findings of the electron microscopist.

The ability of the Golgi material to reduce osmium tetroxide which it does very rapidly is an indication that it may contain unsaturated lipid but then, of course, any reducing substance will reduce osmium tetroxide so this in itself is not a clearcut histochemical test. However, the Golgi material has been stained but rarely with fat dyes, nevertheless the fact that it is soluble in the usual fat solvent suggests that it may contain fatty or lipoidal material. It has been claimed that the Golgi material breaks up after narcosis with chloroform. Monet has shown, that if the germ cells of Helix are treated with sodium bicarbonate, myelin figures are formed from the representatives of the Golgi material (dictyosomes). On the other hand, it has been claimed by Thomas that the dictyosomes of Helix are not Golgi material at all but are formed by the overimpregnation of mitochondria; this is the type of confusion that bedevils the subject of the Golgi apparatus. Ciaccio stained the Golgi apparatus and spermatids with his lipoid technique and Boyle claims that part of the Golgi apparatus of the neurons of Helix are stained by Sudan IV which is a fat stain. Baker carried out a series of detailed histochemical tests on the Golgi material and he found that the apparatus appeared to contain lecithin, cephalin or sphingomyelin and that Windaus' test for cholesterol and Schultz' test for cholesterol were negative. From the foregoing it seems reasonable to suggest that lipoidal material is present in the Golgi apparatus. As long ago as 1925, Nath suggested that the Golgi material contained protein. The same suggestion had been made by Bowen. Gatenby has expressed the opinion that the Golgi material is a combination of protein and lipoid. In fact some authors have found it possible to demonstrate the Golgi apparatus by fat dyes following a prior treatment of the tissue with proteolytic enzymes (pepsin and trypsin). They suggest that these removed the protein which was masking the lipoprotein complex and preventing the lipoid from reacting with the fat dye. Baker using a variety of histochemical tests found that the Golgi apparatus did not contain arginine or glutathione but that it gave a positive reaction with Millon's reagent, a positive xanthoproteic test and also a reaction for tryptophan. However, he found that the Golgi material was not colored more intensely than the cytoplasm so there was not a particular concentration of the amino acids which give these reactions, in the Golgi apparatus.

The localization of vitamin C in the Golgi apparatus has a considerable literature and has been the subject of considerable controversy; for the latest discussion on this subject the reader is referred to a publication by the present author in Protoplasmatologia "Vitamin C in the Animal Cell" and a comparable article in the same volume by Plaut on "Vitamin C in the Plant Cell". Evidence for the occurrence of vitamin C in the Golgi region has also been presented in the chapter on "Mitochondria and the Golgi Complex" in "Cytology and Cell Physiology" (Oxford University Press, 1951). There appears to be a considerable identity in several types of cells between the Golgi preparations and preparations which are demonstrated by the application of the vitamin C reagent (acid silver nitrate). For example, in the neuron of the developing chick the Golgi preparation resembles very closely the result which one gets from application of vitamin C reagent, and in the chick embryo liver a similar correlation can be seen. Diuresis causes changes in position of the Golgi material in rat kidney cells and this is comparable to the distribution of the vitamin C reaction. There is also a similarity of distribution of Golgi material and vitamin C in fibroblast cells and in Goblet cells in the rat colon. Furthermore the distribution of the vitamin C reaction in the ultracentrifuged adrenal, cortical, and medullary cells is identical with the position that is obtained with the Golgi stain. However, as has been mentioned before, the vitamin C reagent is extremely destructive of the cytoplasm of cells and it is very difficult when looking at the effect under the electron microscope to be dogmatic about localization of this material in the Golgi apparatus. Until further evidence is obtained, it is necessary to be conservative about the interpretation of vitamin C reactions in cells.

Some enzymes have been demonstrated to be present in the Golgi apparatus, for instance, it was first shown by the present author in 1943 that the columnar epithelial cells of the guinea pig jejunum contained alkaline phosphatase in the Golgi region. The localization of this enzyme in the same region in the cells of the mantle edge which secretes the shell of the mollusk *Mytilus* was also figured. Various other authors have subsequently recorded the presence of this enzyme in the Golgi region. Deane and Dempsey, for instance, found that alkaline phosphatase was distributed in the Golgi region of the duodenal epithelial cells as granules or as a continuous reticulum. Activity was most intense in the Golgi region at the bases of the villi. Enzyme granules were found in the Golgi region in the cells of the kidney tubules, bile capillaries, and uterine epithelial cells of various mammals, and acid phosphatase has also been demonstrated in the Golgi region of the duodenal cells and in the uterine epithelial cells of pregnant cats and sows. Acid phosphatase has also been found in the Golgi region of the ventral lobe of the prostate by Brandes and Bourne, and details of the influence of the male sex hormone in maintaining its presence in this organelle has already been described. It is of interest that the type of castration change described for the prostate could not be detected by biochemical studies of the cell, so that a biochemical investigation of the effects of castration or male sex hormones on acid phosphatase in the ventral lobe of the prostate would probably have shown no significant change in the level of acid phosphatase in the cells. Yet when this is examined by histochemical methods it can be seen that the most fundamental changes have in fact taken place in the cell and a basic change in the locus of activity of an important enzyme has occurred.

Deane and Dempsey have also demonstrated that adenylic acid phosphatase (presumably 5-nucleotidase) has a similar distribution in the Golgi apparatus of liver cells as glycerophosphatase but it appears at a different pH. These authors suggest that all cells may have significant phosphatase activity in the Golgi zone at some pH and with some substrate. As far as the function of the phosphatase in the Golgi apparatus is concerned nothing certain is known. Emmel has pointed out that the enzyme is present in the lumen of the intestine, kidney tubules, uterus, and bile cavities and suggests that it is being synthesized and excreted by the Golgi complex. This is of course a possibility. It may also be concerned, particularly in the absorptive cells of the gut, with the phosphorylation and dephosphorylation process concerned with the passage of some molecules through the cell membrane. (See Figs. 51, 52, and 53.)

In the last few years the Golgi material which Dalton and Felix have been able to isolate from homogenates of epididymides has provided more specific information concerning its composition—at least in this organ. They found the isolated apparatus to be refringent and part of it to be extractable with 70% alcohol. Another part, however, was insoluble but this part was stainable with Sudan black, indicating some lipid content; presumably it was a lipoprotein. Schneider and Kuff found with identical material that the pentose nucleic acid (RNA), the phospholipid, and the phosphatase concentration in the isolated Golgi fraction was greater than that in the whole tissue. Ascorbic acid, DNA, cytochrome oxidase, and DNAase were absent from the Golgi fraction, but the isolated Golgi material also gave a strong periodic–acid Schiff reaction which seems to have been due to a lipid component. A similar reaction has also been reported in intact cells from Leblond's laboratory.

The structure of the Golgi apparatus in a number of different types of cell is shown in Fig. 54.

In addition to the phosphatase which the Golgi apparatus of most cells has been shown to contain, other enzymes may occur. The present author's studies have demonstrated that oxidative enzymes are often present in the Golgi apparatus of Purkinje and other brain cells. It looks as though the composition of the Golgi apparatus from an enzymic point of view may differ from cell to cell and possibly from time to time, but further studies of this are required.

The relationship of the Golgi apparatus to secretion is shown in Figs. 55 and 56.

The Golgi apparatus in a kidney tubule cell is shown in Fig. 57.

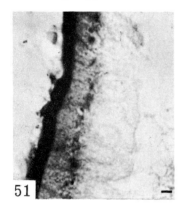

FIG. 51. *Alkaline glycerophosphatase in epithelial cells of small intestine. In addition to reaction in brush border, there is a diffuse reaction in the distal part of the cytoplasm and a distinct reaction in the Golgi region. (Preparation and photograph by present author.)*

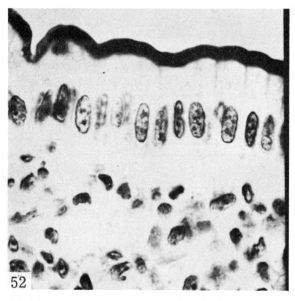

FIG. 52. *Hexoestrol phosphatase in epithelial cell of small intestine. Strong reaction in brush border and nuclei but cytoplasm and Golgi apparatus completely negative. (Preparation and photograph by present author.)*

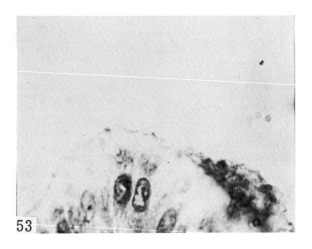

FIG. 53 (above). *Oestrone phosphatase in epithelial cell of small intestine. Strong reaction in nuclei and Golgi material, brush border negative. (Preparation and photograph by present author.)*

FIG. 54 (right). *Electron microscopy of the Golgi apparatus. Different types of apparatus in various cells. a, Renal epithelium, mouse; b, epithelial cell of epididymus, mouse; c, spermatid of cat showing acroblast and acrosome; d, juxtanuclear zone of Golgi apparatus in a human cancer cell; e, portion of a renal epithelial cell of the mouse. The Golgi apparatus appears in the upper center. (From Pollister and Pollister, 1957, Int. Review Cytol., 6, 85.)*

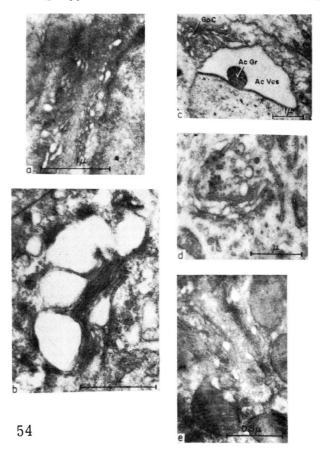

54

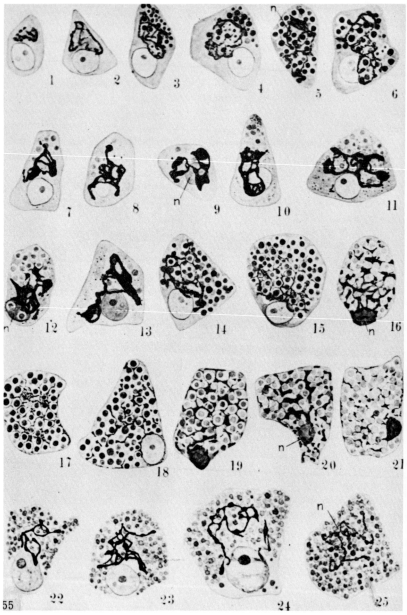

FIG. 55. *Relationship of Golgi apparatus and secretion droplets in parotid gland of cat.* (*From Bowen, 1926, Anat. Rec., 32, 151. By courtesy of the Wistar Institute Press.*)

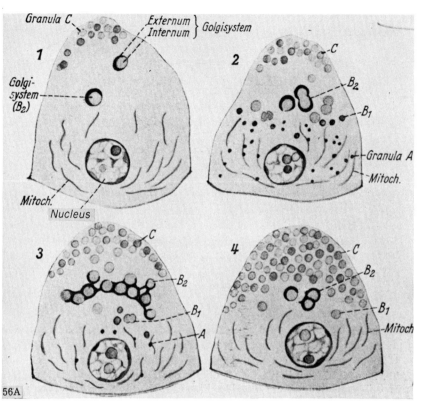

FIG. 56A. *Relationship of the secretion droplets to the Golgi material and mitochondria in the exocrine pancreas cell, according to Hirsch. Note small droplets associated with the mitochondria and moving toward the Golgi region. (From Hirsch, 1939, Form und Stoffwechsel der Golgikorpern. Protoplasma Monographs, Berlin.)*

FIG. 56B. *Production of secretion droplets in Golgi lamellae (after Hirsch). 1. System is resting. 2. The system is building Golgi vacuoles and intermediate bodies. 3. Zymogen granules with membranes produced by Golgi lamellae.*

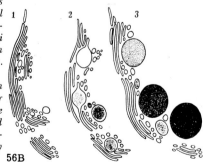

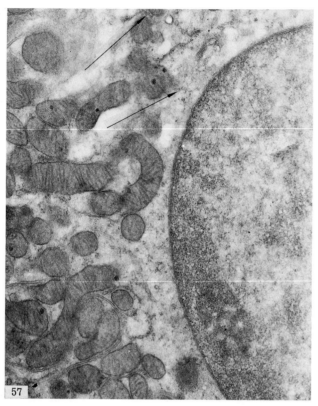

FIG. 57. *Electron micrograph of kidney cell. Note nucleolus near nuclear membrane which shows double structure. Mitochondria present in cytoplasm. Elements of Golgi apparatus in upper part of picture (arrow). (Preparation and photograph by R. Quinton Cox, Dept. of Anatomy, Emory Univ.)*

CHAPTER VI

The nucleus
and the nucleic acids

THE GENERAL MORPHOLOGY
of the nucleus is very well known and need not be considered in great detail here. Under the light microscope it appears to have little structure apart from the existence of refringent nucleoli. In certain kinds of cells, for example, eggs, the existence of nuclear membrane can be detected with the light microscope. Under phase-contrast microscopy more detailed structure can be seen in the nucleus itself and most of this represents the chromatin which with appropriate fixing and staining appears as a network. ⌊The spaces between the network contain what might be described as a "sap" which varies in amount in different types of cells. The shape of the nucleus is usually spherical but may be altered in pathological conditions, and in some organs of senescent animals distorted nuclei can be seen.⌋ In old cells the nucleus may become pyknotic and stain excessively with basic dyes, and under certain physiological conditions the ⌈nuclear shape may change—a classic example of this is the shape of the nuclei of the silk gland cells of the silkworm. Here the tortuous shape of the nucleus, involving as it does a tremendous increase in the area of the membrane, must indicate a considerable degree of nucleocytoplasmic interplay.⌋This subject will be referred to again in much greater

131

detail. (The shape of the nucleus may vary from a rounded spherical to even a branched shape as seen in the silk gland cells of the silkworm or it may even be segmented or have any kind of irregular shape as, for example, in the polymorphonuclear leucocytes of the blood.)

(The nucleus is known to contain two types of nucleic acid, deoxyribonucleic acid and ribonucleic acid. It contains basic proteins and other proteins which include enzymes and, phospholipids, various phosphate compounds and a number of inorganic compounds.)

(There is now a considerable list of enzymes which have been found in the isolated nucleus. These include those which are related to the glycolytic cycle and to the oxidative cycle (although the latter are present in very much smaller amounts than in the cytoplasm). Enzymes concerned with the nucleotide metabolism are naturally present and enzymes which play a part in protein and fat metabolism also occur.) A partial list of the enzymes found in the nuclei is given in Table II. In addition to these biochemical results which have been obtained, studies in the author's laboratory on the distribution of a variety of dephosphorylating enzymes which hydrolyze uridine, inosine, cytidine, and guanosine triphosphates and others which dephosphorylate DPN, TPN, and a wide range of other phosphate esters are present in the nuclei of most cells.

Generally speaking these results indicate, as one might expect, (the presence of most of the enzymes concerned with nucleotide metabolism and with many of those concerned in glycolysis) However there is complete absence of a number of enzymes vital to the functioning of the Krebs cycle, but a surprising concentration of some others such as aconitase. The relatively large amount of cytochrome c is of interest.

In the absence of a Krebs cycle there is some doubt as to whether the nucleus and in particular the nucleolus is able to synthesize ATP, although the nucleus contains plenty of ATPase. (If the nucleolus synthesizes protein) (evidence for this will be presented shortly) it needs ATP. Where does it

TABLE II

Nuclear Enzymes

Enzymes in liver nuclei (unless otherwise stated), activity of total homogenate (%)	Enzymes in liver nuclei (unless otherwise stated), activity of total homogenate (%)
Glycolytic cycle	**Oxidative cycle**
Aldolase, 5–31	Aconitase, 8–14
Fructose-6-phosphatase, 2	Aconitase, 22.5 in cerebral cortex
Glucose-1-phosphatase (nil)	Isocitric dehydrogenase, 2–3
Glyceraldehyde dehydrogenase, (small amount)	Isocitric dehydrogenase, 14.1 in cerebral cortex
α-Glycerophosphate dehydrogenase, up to 22.3	Cytochrome c, 26.3
Hexose diphosphatase (nil)	Cytochrome oxidase, varies from a very low level to 16.5
Pyruvate oxidase, up to 15.4	DPN cytochrome c reductase, 12
	DPN synthesizing enzyme,[a]
Nucleotide metabolism	varies from 69–92
	Fumarase, up to 9.3
Adenosine deaminase, 2.08	α-Ketoglutaric oxidase (a trace)
Adenosine deaminase, 6.0 in heart; other tissues (a trace)	Malic dehydrogenase (very small amount)
Adenosine-3-phosphatase (trace)	Succinic dehydrogenase,[b] 10.1
Adenosine-5-phosphatase, 48 (5-nucleotidase)	TPN cytochrome c reductase, up to 12
ATPase, 10–34	
DNAase, 6.9	**Protein metabolism**
DNAase, 37 in thymus	
Nucleoside phosphorylase (present)	Amine oxidase, 20–30
Ribonuclease, 13.8–49	d-Amino acid oxidase (present)
	Arginase, 36
Fat metabolism	Cathespin, 31.2
	Glutaminase, 14.5
	Leucine amidase, 14.0
Octanoate oxidase, 2.8	Glutamic dehydrogenase, 28
Oxaloacetate oxidase, up to 10.5	

[a] The remarkable concentration of DPN synthesizing enzymes suggests that one of the functions of the nucleus is to supply DPN for the rest of the cell.

[b] It is of interest that histochemical reactions for succinic dehydrogenase in most cells show no trace of the reaction in the nuclei.

get it from? The mitochondria have all the equipment for the production of ATP, and it has been noted that in tissue culture cells the nucleolus frequently moves in the nucleus to touch the nuclear membrane. Mitochondria have often been observed to touch the nuclear membrane at the same spot and at the same time as the nucleolus, and it has already been suggested that perhaps ATP is passed across the nuclear membrane at this time. It is of interest that Tewari and the present author have shown that in spinal ganglion cells there appears to be a cycle of activity between the nucleolus and the mitochondria. When the nucleolus moves to the side of the nucleus and touches the nuclear membrane, the mitochondria are clustered around the nucleus. The nucleolus then passes to the center of the nucleus and the mitochondria disperse through the cytoplasm. At the same time droplets of unidentified material make their appearance in the cytoplasm.

Before 1950, the electron microscope had given us very little help as far as the structure of the nuclear membrane was concerned, but during that year Callan and Tomlin were able to dissect out the large nuclei of the germinal vesicle of the oöcytes of amphibian eggs. These nuclei were ruptured by exerting a slight pressure on them, and the broken nuclear membranes so obtained were then examined under the electron microscope. By using this technique they found that the nuclear membrane actually contained pores. Callan and Tomlin then found that the nuclear membrane was composed of two sheets, an outer one in which the pores were present and an inner continuous sheet; these pores were approximately 400 A in diameter. Pores of this type have also been found in the oocytes of the starfish and in sea urchin eggs; the nuclear membranes of pancreatic cells have also been said to contain such pores. It has been claimed that neurons possess as many as 10,000 pores in each nucleus. Although there has been some discussion about the reality of the existence of these pores, it is fairly certain now that they do occur more or less universally (see Fig. 58).

FIG. 58. *Electron micrograph of rat liver cell. Note pores in nuclear membrane. (Courtesy of the Phillips Co., Eindhoven, Netherlands.)*

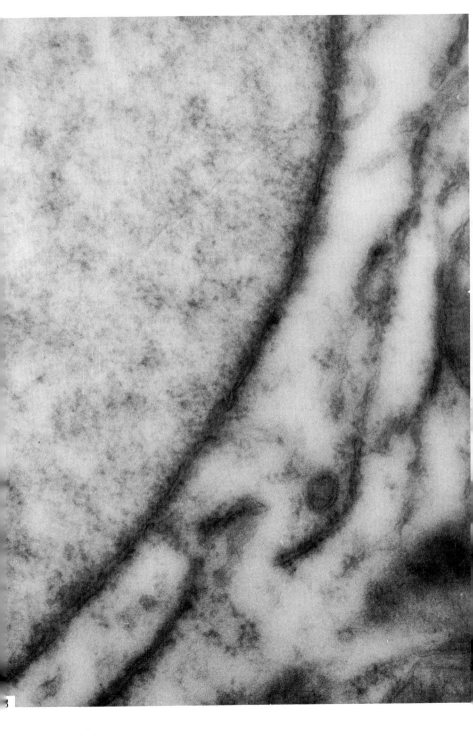

The dimensions of the nuclear membrane are of interest. Under the electron microscope the membrane can be seen to be composed of two osmiophilic layers with a clear layer in-between. Each of the osmiophilic layers has a thickness of 70 to 80 A and the nonosmiophilic space between them ranges from 100 to 150 A. It is of great interest that this is practically identical with the dimensions of the intracytoplasmic membranes (endoplasmic reticulum) and it has, in fact, been suggested by Watson that the nuclear membrane is not a separate membranous structure at all but is simply a part of the endoplasmic reticular membrane. If these can themselves be regarded as extensions of the cytoplasmic membrane then the nucleus is really enveloped in what is a deep and complex fold of the cell membrane.

The specific details of the nuclear membrane vary considerably in different types of cells but, generally speaking, the three-layered structure of the membrane and the presence of pores are characters that can be accepted for most nuclear membranes examined to date. The nucleus of nondividing cells has been referred to as being in a "resting" condition, and this is singularly inappropriate in view of the metabolic activity which this organelle must be carrying out almost continuously.

The relationship of the volume of the nucleus to that of the cytoplasm varies considerably in different types of cells, and, generally speaking, the volume of cytoplasm increases by comparison with the nuclear volume as the cells age.

Nuclei which are fixed by standard histological and cytological fixatives show a nuclear reticulum on which are scattered basophilic staining substances which have been described classically as chromatin, and the parts of the reticulum which do not show basophilic staining have been referred to as "linin." In and around this network it has been assumed that nuclear sap, which has been described as the "karyolymph" or "enchylema," exists.

The other obvious structure in the nucleus which can be seen is the nucleolus. There may be one or more of these and they vary considerably in shape. The nucleolus was first described as long ago as 1781 by Fontana and from then on it seems to have been pretty generally recognized as a typical cell structure. Nucleoli under the light microscope usually have the appearance of rounded homogeneous structures always within the nucleus, but Tewari and the present author have seen them attached to the outside of the nuclear membrane in spinal ganglion cells. There appear to be two structural phases in the nucleolus, one is in the form of a series of highly coiled strands and the other a structureless phase, presumably some sort of a nucleolar sap. This nucleolar sap is called the "pars amorpha" and the coiled strand is the nucleolonema described by Estable of Monte Video and his co-workers. The nucleolus contains a good deal of ribonucleic acid and there is also some evidence that it contains deoxyribonucleic acid as well. Caspersson has claimed that it is rich in diamino acids, and the presence of protein masked phospholipids has also been described; in the spinal ganglion cells the nucleolus stains intensely with mitochondrial techniques, but further details of the chemical nature of the nucleolus will be given later on. The nucleolus varies in shape and size according to the activity of the cell, during the period of anabolism it is said to become hypertrophied and during the catabolic stage it is said to become reduced in size. The nucleolus shows changes with pH, a number of drugs cause it to change in size, and it is also affected by ionizing radiations. Although the nucleolus is an area in the nucleus where there is a great concentration of special substances, the electron microscope up to date has given no evidence that it is surrounded by a limiting membrane, this is not quite what one would expect and so perhaps it is necessary to be careful in discussing nuclear–nucleolar interrelationships until the significance of this fact is assessed. In the interphase nucleus, the nucleolus retains its characteristic spherical shape, and, provided the cell is not subjected to any particular type of stress, the size and general appearance of the nucleolus will remain unchanged. During the prophase stage of cell division, the nucleolus demonstrates a relationship to a

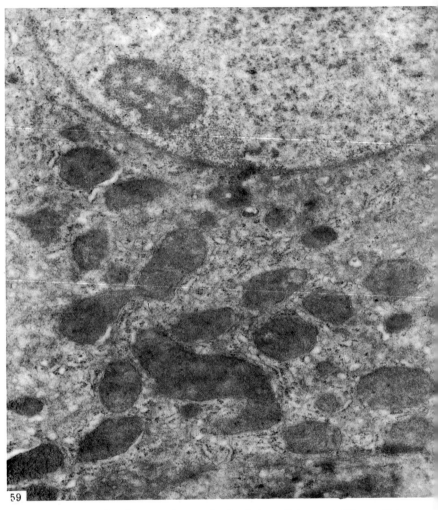

59

FIG. 59. *Electron micrograph of tubular cell from rat kidney. Note RNA granules apparently passing through nuclear membrane to right of nucleolus and in the portion of the nuclear membrane to the right. (Preparation and photograph by R. Quinton Cox, Dept. of Anatomy, Emory Univ.)*

specific chromosome as it develops. With the onset of metaphase at a time when the nuclear membrane dissolves away, the nucleolus disappears or ceases to be evident as a formed structure. At telophase, just before the nuclei re-form, small basophilic bodies appear between the chromosomes which form up to produce the nucleolus again. One of the most characteristic inclusions in the nucleolus is the vacuole —a structure which seems very resistant to most of the staining agents. Darker staining areas within the nucleolus are known as nucleolini. Although there is some evidence that the nucleolus is in a semifluid state, it has a considerable density and can be centrifuged to one end of the nucleus and more or less pure nucleolar material can be obtained by differential centrifugation. The studies with x-ray absorption and ultraviolet absorption suggest that the nucleolus is a semisolid body and that it contains proteins which are in a state of considerable dehydration. It is of interest that in cells which engage in active synthetic activity the nucleoli become hypertrophied, and cells which are not actively synthetic have little or no nucleoli. The classic example of this can be found in the case of muscle. Embryonic cells which are forming muscle fibers have very well defined nucleoli, presumably because they are concerned in synthesizing muscle protein whereas the nuclei in muscle fibers of adult animals show very few nucleoli and those which are present are extremely small. Starvation also causes a great reduction in size of nucleoli but they increase in size very substantially on refeeding, suggesting again that protein synthesis is taking place. In embryonic tissue, nucleoli always become most obvious at the time when the tissue is differentiating, presumably at the time when specially differentiated protein for building up a specific organ is being made. There is some evidence that either whole nucleoli or nucleolar material can be passed from the nucleus into the cytoplasm (see Fig. 59). This has been recorded both for fixed and for fresh tissues, and Duryee (1950) mentions that it takes place in the living oocytes of

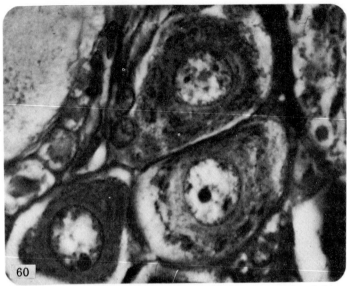

FIG. 60. *Spinal ganglion cells of rat, mercury bromophenol blue reaction for proteins, showing nucleolus in contact with nuclear membrane. (Preparation and photographs by H. B. Tewari, Dept. of Anatomy, Emory Univ.)*

amphibia. Tewari and the present author have seen it in spinal ganglion cells (see Figs. 60 and 61). It, therefore, appears quite possible that this may occur and will be referred to again later.

The rest of the nucleus is composed of nucleoplasm which does not appear to have a highly organized structure as demonstrated under the electron microscope but rather seems to be built up of irregularly distributed particles of various sizes although their average diameter according to Sjöstrand is 170 A. The range of variation being 150–190 A.

CHROMOSOMES

Chromosomes appear to organize themselves out of the reticulum of the nucleus during the process of mitosis, and during the preliminary stage of the prophase they become shorter and detach themselves from any reticular material left in the nucleus. Subsequently, with the disappearance of the nuclear membrane, the nuclear sap diffuses into and becomes mixed with the cytoplasmic materials. At this stage production of a spindle begins and the chromosomes lie free in the cytoplasm and then become organized in relation to the spindle which forms around them. Chromosomes are bodies which have been known for a very long time and even those of the insects have been known since the middle of the 19th century. Insect salivary gland chromosomes are extremely large and show a very complex banding which appears to be related to the location of the genes (see Fig. 62). These bands appear to contain DNA and can be demonstrated by a number of staining methods.

The persistence of chromosomes in the resting nucleus has been a problem to cytologists for many years, and studies with ultraviolet absorption on the nuclei of living cells have demonstrated that at least the DNA of the chromosomes is still present at this stage. If resting nuclei are broken up and ultracentrifuged, fine filaments can be obtained from them, and it appears that these are probably greatly extended chromosomes. Certainly there is some evidence that typical chromosome structures are present in them. The bands which are shown to be present on chromosomes are known as euchromatic bands and heterochromatic bands. The former were said to be composed of DNA associated with histones, and the heterochromatin appears to contain both DNA and RNA. Curious types of chromosomes known as lampbrush chromosomes have been described in the eggs of amphibia, fish, reptiles, and birds and they, like the other types of chromosomes, are banded but also have a number of loops which project from the surface and extend into the nuclear sap in which the chromosomes lie. These chromosomes are extremely long and very thin and they develop their particular shape just about the time when yolk is being synthesized actively by the egg. At this time, too, the nucleus appears to contain quite a number of nucleoli, and it is thought that these are produced

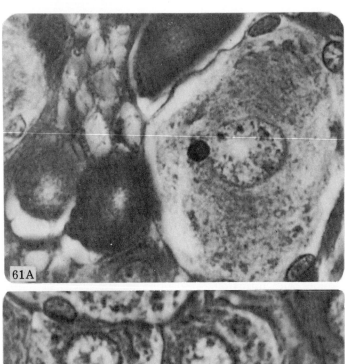

61A

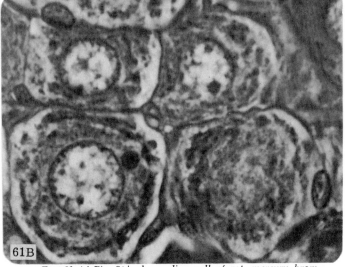

61B

Fig. 61 (*A-D*). *Spinal ganglion cell of rat, mercury brom-phenol blue reaction for proteins. Showing passage of nucleolus out of nucleus to periphery of cytoplasm. (Preparation*

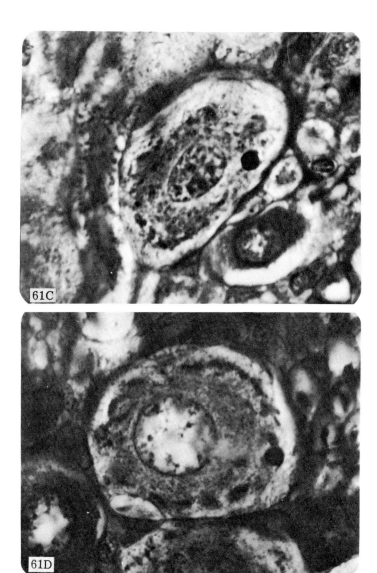

and photographs by H. B. Tewari, Dept. of Anatomy, Emory
Univ.)

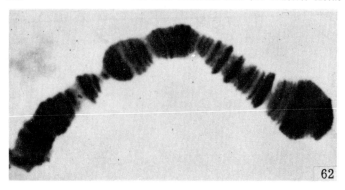

FIG. 62. *Portion of a salivary gland chromosome in* Chironomus. *The dark bands represent localization of DNA. (From White, "Cytology and Cell Physiology," 2nd Edition, 1951, Oxford Univ. Press.)*

by specialized regions in the chromosomes. When oogenesis is complete the chromosomes shrink and become very much thicker and the number of nucleoli becomes reduced. The main axis of the lampbrush chromosome contains a considerable amount of DNA, and the loops which project into the cytoplasm seem to be composed largely of RNA. It has been demonstrated by Ficq (1955a) that precursors of RNA and proteins which have been labeled with radioactive atoms are localized more in the nucleus than in the cytoplasm and that the incorporation of, for example, adenine into RNA seems to be localized almost exclusively in the loops of the lampbrush chromosomes. It seems pretty certain that the loops of these chromosomes represent highly active areas which are specifically concerned with the synthesis of protein.

This discussion of chromosomes leads us on to the concept of the gene. It appears to be generally accepted that genes can be described chemically as nucleoproteins. The difficulty, however, is to find some way of explaining why these various genes are able to exert, either by chemical alterations, or physical structure, their different activities. It has been suggested that the difference in the proteins associated with the DNA in each of the genes is the important factor. At least this was originally thought to be the case, but there is now a good deal of evidence that suggests that the difference is really not one which exists among the proteins. It is thought that the DNA may vary from the point of view of the sequence of nucleotides in the nucleic acid or in the spatial relationship of the nucleotides to each other; the length of the nucleotide chain which makes up the DNA may also be important. Stern has suggested that one of the analogies concerning the genes was that the relationship of the different organization of DNA to production of different types of genes was "the analogy of the sound track traced in a plastic matrix by a recording stylus, the modulated grooves would be the counterpart of genic modulations engraved on a chemically uniform nuclear protein matrix." According to this point of view the various genes would represent isomers or stereoisomers of each other.

We have mentioned RNA and DNA frequently and we should now consider these substances in a little more detail. They are both nucleic acids and constituents, not only of the nucleus but of the nucleolus as well and RNA is also present in the cytoplasm in association with the endoplasmic reticulum as ribonucleoprotein granules and it also occurs scattered through the rest of the cytoplasm.

The discovery and identification of nucleic acids began with the work of Miescher in the last half of the 19th century and our knowledge of the structure and function of these acids has developed from this point. Nucleic acids are found in all living cells, not only in animals but also in plants, and are associated with proteins to form nucleoproteins.

Nucleic acids are actually polymers, being composed of a very large number of nucleotides which represent the monomeric part of the polymer. They all have a basic chemical structure being composed firstly of a base which can be either a purine or a pyrimidine, secondly a sugar, and thirdly a phosphate group. There are two types of sugar present in nucleic acids, *d*-ribose and deoxyribose, and

HCOH
|
HCOH
|
HCOH   O   or
|
HC————
|
CH₂OH

D-Ribose (α-D-ribofuranose)

HCOH
|
CH₂
|
HCOH   O   or
|
HC————
|
CH₂OH

D-2-Deoxyribose (α-D-2-deoxyribofuranose)

nucleic acids have been divided into two main groups according to which type of sugar they possess. Those containing the ribose are known as ribonucleic acid and are represented in short-hand terminology as RNA and those containing the second type of sugar are called desoxyribonucleic acid and are given the symbol DNA. Some people use the term pentose nucleic acid for RNA and give it the symbol PNA and this difference in nomenclature sometimes leads to confusion among the uninitiated in this field. There are 5 bases associated with nucleotides of which two (adenine and guanine) are purines and three (uracil, thymine, and cytosine) are pyrimidines.

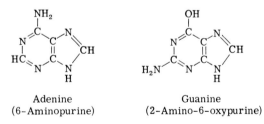

Adenine
(6-Aminopurine)

Guanine
(2-Amino-6-oxypurine)

Uracil
(2, 4-Dioxypyrimidine)

Thymine
(5-Methyl-2, 4-dioxypyrimidine)

Cytosine
(2-Oxy-4-aminopyrimidine)

Originally DNA was obtained from the thymus because of the high concentration of nuclei in such a gland and was called thymonucleic acid, and the RNA was obtained from yeast and was called yeast nucleic acid. It was thus thought that the DNA was characteristic of animals and RNA characteristic of vegetable tissues, however, it has now been found that both DNA and RNA are present in both animal and plant cells but are distributed differently. DNA is concentrated more in the nuclei and this is why DNA was the type of nucleic acid isolated when thymus gland was used as a source.

In the formation of nucleotides, compounds known as nucleosides are first produced. A nucleoside is a molecule which is formed by the combination between a base which can be either a purine or pyrimidine and one or other of the two sugars, i.e., adenine, guanine, cytosine, uracil, or thymine associated with a sugar will produce a nucleoside; if they are associated with the ribose sugar they are one type of compound and with the deoxyribose they form another type of compound. Adenine, for instance, with ribose forms adenosine and with deoxyribose it forms deoxyadenosine; guanine forms guanosine with ribose and deoxyguanosine with deoxyribose; cytosine becomes cytidine with the sugar and deoxycytidine with the deoxy sugar; uracil with the ribose sugar forms uridine but the corresponding compound with the deoxyribose, is not recorded. Thymine forms thymidine with ribose.

Adenosine (9-β-ribofuranosidoadenine)

The next stage in the formation of a nucleotide is the combination of a phosphate with the nucleoside. For instance, adenosine can have one, two, or three phosphates attached to it and it then becomes adenosine monophosphate, diphosphate, or triphosphate, respectively. Similarly the other compounds mentioned can be mono-, di-, or triphosphorylated. Phosphorylation of the five bases with a single phosphate group forms adenylic, guanylic, cytidylic, uradylic, and thymidylic acids and isomers of these are also known. The adenylic acid is commonly spoken of as "muscle" adenylic acid because it was first isolated from muscle. It is one of the structural units of ribonucleic acid and its phosphoric linkage is to the 5-carbon atom. In plants, however, the phosphate linkage in the monophosphate appears to be largely associated with the 3-carbon atom.

The various nucleotides mentioned in the foregoing become polymerized by the formation of phosphoric acid bonds between the sugars, and polynucleotides are thus formed. The common name for these is "nucleic acids." When the nucleotides are made from deoxyribose sugars,

FIG. 63 (*top*). *Distribution of DNA and RNA, two substances that determine the form and function of cells. DNA (broken hatching) and RNA (solid hatching) are both found in chromosomes. RNA migrates (solid arrows) often via the nucleolus and nuclear membrane into the cytoplasmic membranes, where it presides over protein synthesis. DNA leaves the nucleus (broken arrow) only in certain cells. (Figures and legend from Gay, "Nuclear Control of the Cell," Scientific American, January 1960.)*

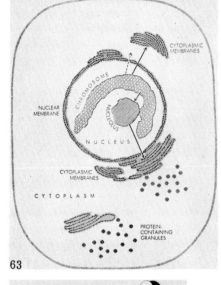

FIG. 64 (*bottom*). *Model of molecular structure of DNA, according to Feughelman et al., 1955. (From Brachet, 1957, "Biochemical Cytology," Academic Press, New York.)*

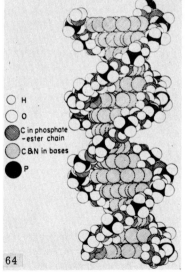

the deoxynucleic (also referred to as desoxynucleic) acids (DNA) are formed and if the ribose sugar is involved ribose nucleic acid (RNA) is obtained.

The structure of these two compounds can be diagrammatically demonstrated,

RNA

Base	Base	Base	Base
OH	OH	OH	OH
PO$_4$	PO$_4$	PO$_4$	PO$_4$
ribose	ribose	ribose	ribose

The bases in each nucleotide vary and may be any one of those first mentioned (i.e., adenine, guanine, cytosine, or uracil). The frequency of each in any particular RNA molecule depends upon the origin of the RNA.

The distribution of DNA and RNA in cells is shown in Fig. 63.

DNA has fundamentally the same structure as RNA but lacks the OH groups shown as attached to the sugars in RNA and uses the three bases—adenine, guanine, and cytosine but replaces the uracil by thymine.

The formula for DNA looks like this, that is it is very similar to RNA.

DNA

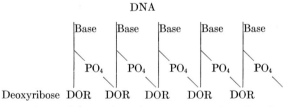

Preparations of DNA have been examined under the electron microscope and have been seen to have the form of long fibers with a narrow diameter of about 20 A across.

The structure of the DNA molecule suggested by Watson and Crick is that it is formed of two spirals which are coiled about a common axis and the union between the spirals is by means of hydrogen bonds between the bases of the nucleotides. The phosphates and sugars are actually on the outside of the chain while the bases are located inside it (see Fig. 64). The structure of RNA is not so clear cut but there is some evidence which suggests that the molecule may have a branched structure. The suggested attachments of the two DNA chains in the spiral is through their individual bases and certain bases couple with specific bases, e.g., adenine and thymine, and cytosine and guanine must be opposite each other. (See Fig. 65.) The structure therefore is something like this.

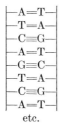

The order and frequency of bases shown is empirical and would depend on the origin of DNA. We do not yet have a technique for determining the order of bases in the nucleic acids. RNA has not been proved yet to exist as double strands but many attempts are being made to find out for certain whether this is so.

In the living cell the nucleic acids are inevitably combined with proteins to form nucleoproteins and again because of the nature of the sugar one can specify two types of nucleoprotein, deoxyribonucleoprotein and the ribonucleoprotein. The main protein which combines with DNA in these complexes is of a basic nature and is usually either histone or protamine, and there are varying amounts of protein and DNA combined under different circumstances.

It is of interest that viruses and bacteriophages are largely composed of nucleic acids, and in the case of the bacteriophages the DNA can be extruded from the virus particle into the bacterial cell where it can lead to formation of fresh virus but this will be mentioned again later.

NUCLEIC ACIDS OF THE NUCLEUS

DNA is segregated away from the cytoplasm within the nucleus, although, as we have seen, the isolation of the

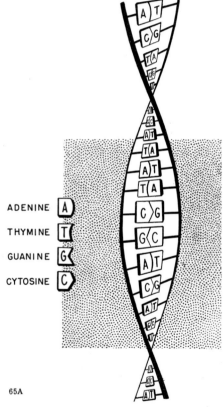

FIG. 65 *A and B. Section of DNA helix to show base-pair sequences.* (*Fig. 65A from "Medical News," May 11, 1960, Supplement on Nucleic Acids. Fig. 65B from Rassegna Medica 37, 228, 1960.*)

nucleus from the cytoplasm is by no means complete since there are a number of pores which are present in the nuclear membrane and which lead into the cytoplasm as such. But the significant thing about DNA is that practically all of it in the cell is localized in the nucleus and it is the DNA that has the major genetic function in the cell.

What evidence do we have that DNA is concerned with heredity? The evidence for this has been excellently presented by Brachet in his book "Biochemical Cytology" and will be summarized here.

Seven points in evidence for this are:

1. There is a specificity of DNA's from different species.

2. There is a specific localization of DNA on chromosomes, e.g., in *Drosophila* there is an identity between the DNA bands and the localization of the genes.

3. There is an approximate constancy of amount of DNA per chromosome set.

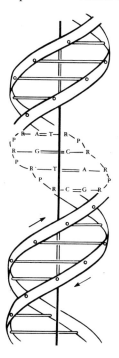

RNA and DNA

Nucleic acid, which forms part of the composition of viruses, may be present in the form of RNA (ribonucleic acid) or DNA (desoxyribonucleic acid). In general, according to their type, the viruses contain only one or other form of nucleic acid; however, examples are known containing both, as in the case of the influenza virus. DNA is a tetranucleotide consisting of:

$H_3 PO_4 \cdot R \cdot$ guanine — $H_3 PO_4 \cdot R \cdot$ thymine — $H_3 PO_4 \cdot R \cdot$ cytosine — $H_3 PO_4 \cdot R \cdot$ adenine

where R indicates desoxyribose, while in the case of ribonucleic acid (RNA) it stands for ribose.

At the left is the systematic representation (from Wilkins, 1956) of the DNA molecule, formed of two pentose-phosphate chains winding helicoidally around a central axis and joined by means of pairs of bases—adenine and thymine, guanine and cytosine.

A fraction of the DNA molecule is represented below, with the pairs of bases joining the pentose-phosphate rings.

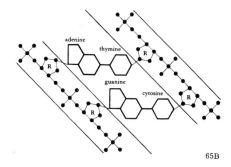

4. DNA is relatively metabolically stable.

5. Mutagenic agents affect DNA.

6. DNA plays a role in a phage reproduction.

7. Bacterial transforming agents have been identified with DNA.

With regard to point 1, striking differences were seen in the composition of bases in various DNA's which were isolated from different species of animals. Point 2, the localization of DNA as demonstrated by the Feulgen reaction and its relationship to the genetic areas has been demonstrated. Point 3, some constancy does occur, it is not absolute but there is a marked tendency toward such a constancy. Point 4, DNA is probably the most stable of the phosphorus compounds that are found in the cell and is very much more stable than RNA. Point 5, all agents which have a mutagenic effect, for example, nitrogen mustard, ultraviolet rays, x-rays, affect DNA. Most of the points quoted so far are circumstantial but point 6, the role of DNA in phage reproduction, seems to provide more direct evidence, as will be explained here. Some investigators, e.g., Hershey and Chase, labeled DNA with P^{32} (radioactive phosphorus) and its protein with S^{35} (radioactive sulfur). The phages used (T2 type) have a head and a tail; the membrane of the head is made of protein and contain DNA (see Figs. 66 and 67). When the phage is added to the bacteria which it infects, the tail of the phage becomes attached to the membrane of the bacterium by a submicroscopic sucker. The tail of the phage has recently been shown to be cross striated and contractile and to contain a solid core. Contraction of the tail shoots the core; like a harpoon, into the bacterium. Attached to the proximal part of the core is one end of a long, single, greatly folded, DNA molecule which occupies the head of the phage. The solid core carries this molecule into the substance of the bacterium just as a harpoon carries with it the rope to which it is attached. Practically no protein enters with the DNA, and the DNA then takes over the synthetic process

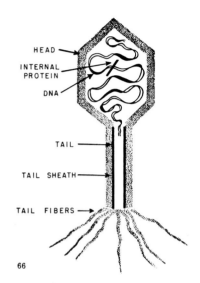

Fig. 66 *(right). Infection of bacteria with T_2 virus particles. Diagram of single virus. Note DNA in the head. (From "Medical News," May 11, 1960, Supplement on Nucleic Acids.)*

Fig. 67 *(below). Results of T_2 virus invasion. Note how DNA of virus diverts metabolism of bacterium into reproduction of virus DNA and protein. (From "Medical News," May 11, 1960. Supplement on Nucleic Acids.)*

HEAD

INTERNAL PROTEIN

DNA

TAIL

TAIL SHEATH

TAIL FIBERS

66

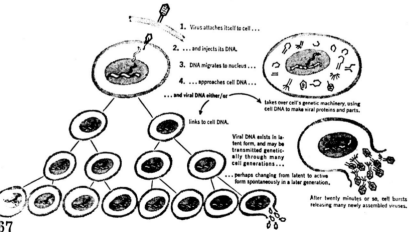

1. Virus attaches itself to cell . . .

2. . . . and injects its DNA.

3. DNA migrates to nucleus . . .

4. . . . approaches cell DNA . . .

. . . and viral DNA either/or

takes over cell's genetic machinery, using cell DNA to make viral proteins and parts.

links to cell DNA.

Viral DNA exists in latent form, and may be transmitted genetically through many cell generations . . .

. . . perhaps changing from latent to active form spontaneously in a later generation.

After twenty minutes or so, cell bursts releasing many newly assembled viruses.

67

of the bacterial cell and uses its metabolism to produce some virus protein and a good deal of its own DNA instead of bacterial protein. Thus the DNA of the phage is able to produce DNA which is genetically identical to the infecting bacteriophage and genetically quite different from the DNA of the bacterium.

Point 7, the significance of DNA for bacterial transformations is explained as follows. There are two types of pneumococci, one type known as the encapsulated or smooth strain and a second type which is not capsulated and is known as the rough strain. If DNA from the first of these bacteria is brought into contact with the rough strain of Pneumococcus, the latter will be converted into the smooth strain and this property will be transmitted to the descendants of the transformed strains and these descendants will produce DNA with the same properties. Thus the DNA is found to be directly concerned with the synthesis of a particular type of capsule. Bacterial transformations have also been obtained with a number of other bacteria using DNA.

This work has suggested that at least some and possibly all the genes found in bacteria were probably completely or largely composed of DNA.

It is of interest that bacterial viruses (bacteriophages) are all DNA viruses, that plant viruses are all RNA viruses, and that some human viruses contain RNA and some contain DNA.

It has previously been mentioned that the model for DNA was a two stranded molecule arranged in a helical form with the pairs of bases held together by hydrogen bonds, for example, adenine would combine with thymine and guanine with cytosine. This is a sort of zipper arrangement and if these pairs of molecules could be unzipped by breaking the hydrogen bonds, then each of the members of the chain could serve as a template for the manufacture of a second chain. This is the type of molecular arrangement that would be necessary to enable a gene to reproduce itself, and there is very strong evidence that DNA molecules could, in fact, be equated with genes. Although DNA fulfills these requirements, we cannot be sure, of

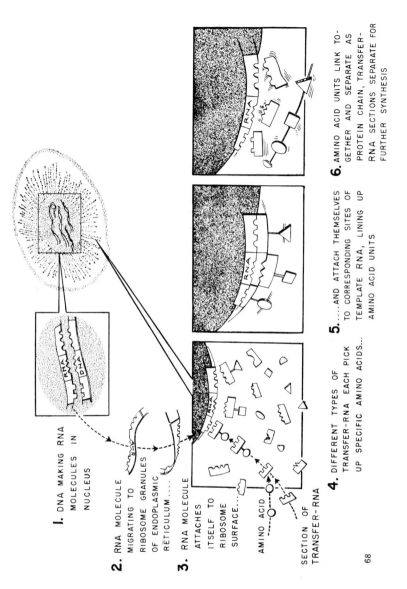

1. DNA MAKING RNA MOLECULES IN NUCLEUS

2. RNA MOLECULE MIGRATING TO RIBOSOME GRANULES OF ENDOPLASMIC RETICULUM.....

3. RNA MOLECULE ATTACHES ITSELF TO RIBOSOME SURFACE.....

AMINO ACID

SECTION OF TRANSFER-RNA

4. DIFFERENT TYPES OF TRANSFER-RNA EACH PICK UP SPECIFIC AMINO ACIDS...

5. ....AND ATTACH THEMSELVES TO CORRESPONDING SITES OF TEMPLATE RNA, LINING UP AMINO ACID UNITS

6. AMINO ACID UNITS LINK TO-GETHER AND SEPARATE AS PROTEIN CHAIN, TRANSFER-RNA SECTIONS SEPARATE FOR FURTHER SYNTHESIS

68

FIG. 68. *Schematic diagram of the role of the DNA and RNA in protein synthesis.* (From "Medical News," May 11, 1960. Supplement on Nucleic Acids.)

course, that when it is incorporated into the cell it simply exists as DNA. Most likely it combines with a protein which probably exerts an influence on the DNA in its function as a gene.

Although the synthesis of protein in a cell is attributed largely to RNA, there is some evidence that DNA is concerned with this process and that it is particularly concerned with the sequence of the arrangement of amino acids in the protein being synthesized (see Fig. 68); but it is thought that even this activity on the part of DNA is mediated by RNA. In experiments in which bacteria were disrupted, it was found that incorporation of amino acids into protein required the presence of DNA before it could take place but that RNA also appeared to be necessary.

One very difficult and complex problem to explain is the mechanism by which the gene, if it is composed largely or exclusively of DNA, is able to pass on the genetic information which it contains so that the various cells conform to the genetic requirements. In this connection the reader should study Danielli's interesting discussion on the theory of nucleocytoplasmic relationship (Exp. Cell Research, supp. 6, 1959, p. 252). The important thing about the DNA molecule is not so much its length as the sequence of nucleotides in it. This information must be transferred and it is the proteins to which this transfer is made. Probably what happens is that the DNA molecule and its sequence of nucleotides decide the sequence of amino acids in the proteins which are being built up. It is thought that this is not done directly but that the information is first transferred from the DNA to the RNA, and it is the RNA which serves as the template. The problem of the relation of RNA to protein synthesis will be discussed shortly. It appears possible that each region or nucleotide sited at a particular point on the RNA template binds a specific amino acid, and the sequence of these amino acids is determined by the sequence of the sites on the RNA. The intensity of these reactions is noteworthy, genetic effects are well known to be most resistant to unstable conditions, particularly environmental disorders. Genetic information tends to exert its effect despite the subjection of the organism concerned to variations in temperature, salinity of the fluids with which it comes in contact, different types of food, the amount of light it receives, exposure to toxic substances, and so on. However, radiation is one environmental factor which can exert a profound effect on the genetic material.

An interesting thing concerning the passing on of genetic information to the organism by the DNA is that there is no feedback of information to inform the DNA, so far as we know, of what has been done or what needs to be done but, nevertheless, practically all significant cell activity is affected by the gene. It is certainly a very complex physicochemical problem and there is still a very long way to go before it can be adequately understood. Most interesting from the point of view of the subject of this book is the fact that the DNA, tucked away in the nucleus as it is, can exert its effect throughout the cell, not only determining the type of protein which is laid down in the cell during the process of development but controlling a large proportion of the activities of the cell in the adult animal.

Those interested in what may be called the storage and activation of genetic information should read an article by Henry Quastler which forms a part of the Conference on "Chemical Organization of Cells Normal and Abnormal" published in Lab. Investig. 1959, and also Danielli's review (already mentioned).

RIBOSE NUCLEIC ACID (RNA)

Just as DNA is thought to carry information concerning the race, it has been suggested recently that RNA is concerned with carrying information concerning the individual, in other words the RNA molecules are concerned with the process of storing information. It has in fact been suggested that memory is stored in the RNA of the neurons of the brain. This, however, is largely theoretical at the moment but is an intriguing prospect for further investigation.

There seems now to be extremely good evidence that

RNA is concerned with the synthesis of protein. Before we go on to consider this perhaps we should say a word about the nature of protein.

If proteins are hydrolyzed they break down to amino acids and under natural circumstances a protein is made up of amino acids joined together in the form of elongated chains known as polypeptide chains. In a protein of molecular weight of about 25,000 there will be, according to F.H.C. Crick, something like 230 residues joined end-to-end to form the single polypeptide chain of which the molecule is made. The amino acids are invariably joined together in this chain by the same method. The bonds are covalent bonds and the amino acids are joined together by the formation of a peptide link which results in the elimination of a molecule of water; nearly all covalent links in a protein are formed by this method, however, occasionally there are links between two sulfur molecules. The protein so formed therefore is an elongated linear molecule, and Crick points out that there is no evidence that it is branched. Crick also makes the point that there are only about 20 different kinds of amino acids in proteins but these same 20 occur, generally speaking, in practically all proteins—it does not matter whether the proteins come from animals or plants or micro-organisms. He points out, however, that not all proteins contain all these amino acids but the majority of proteins do contain a proportion of them. Another point is that all the amino acids present in proteins have the L-configuration. There are some specific amino acids which occur only in specific proteins and probably the best example of these is hydroxyproline, the amino acid which is characteristically found in collagen. The twenty amino acids found universally in proteins are as follows: glycine, alanine, valine, leucine, isoleucine, proline, phenylalanine, tyrosine, serine, threonine, asparagine, glutamine, aspartic acid, glutamic acid, arginine, lysine, histidine, tryptophane, cysteine, methionine. Other amino acids which may be present are: hydroxyproline, hydroxylysine, phosphoserine, diaminotumelic acid, thyroxine, and cystine. Crick points out in his article that not only is the composition of a particular protein fixed but it appears that the order of the amino acids in the polypeptide chain is determined very exactly and that, for example, every molecule of hemoglobin in human blood has precisely the same sequence of amino acids as every other molecule of hemoglobin. A further point is that the polypeptide chains of the proteins are not extended but are folded upon each other, and this folding is said to be maintained by physical bonds which are weak in nature and possibly also by disulfide linkages and other linkages may exist as well. The degree of folding is thought to be similar for each particular protein, and presumably the denaturation of proteins results in the destruction of this folding. If any one of the twenty essential amino acids is supplied to a cell, it can be incorporated into proteins but if, for example, any one of the twenty is not available to an organism, protein synthesis cannot occur. Not only is the synthesis of that part of the protein molecule which does contain the specific amino acid prevented but also that part of the molecule which does not contain the amino acid is also not synthesized. Crick points out that, with this type of mechanism and with the order of the amino acids being very specific, one would expect that some variation or mistakes in order would occur occasionally, but as he points out the information we have at the moment is that such mistakes are very infrequent.

Although all the hemoglobin molecules of the human being are the same, if this hemoglobin is compared with that of the horse or some other animal, it will be found that there is a general similarity of pattern between the two molecules and that the amino acid composition will be pretty much the same for both of them. These two hemoglobin molecules may differ a little in their electrophoretic properties—their crystalline form may differ and the ends on their polypeptide chains may be different, but it is very likely that the sequence of amino acids in the polypeptide chains will be fundamentally the same except for one or two slight alterations in the sequence. It is of interest that this

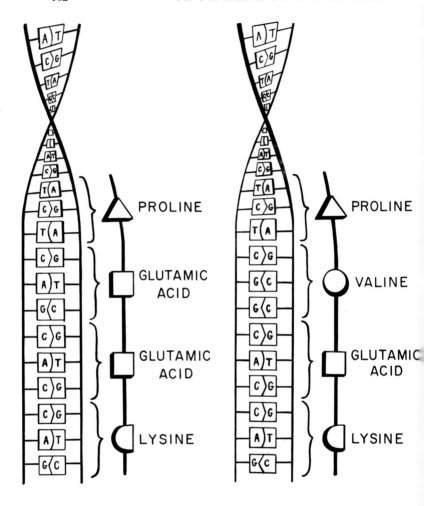

69 NORMAL DNA   ABNORMAL DNA

Fɪɢ. 69. *Synthesis of normal and sickle cell hemoglobin. (From "Medical News," May 11, 1960. Supplement on Nucleic Acids.)*

produces what might be described as a family likeness between proteins, and Crick suggests that it may be that "these sequences are the most delicate expression possible of the phenotype of an organism and that vast amounts of evolutionary information may be hidden away within them." It seems possible, and this will be further discussed, that the sequence of amino acids in the proteins is under control of Mendelian genes and the classic case of this has, in fact, been described by Pauling and his co-workers in 1949.

It was found that the nature of the protein in the hemoglobin in human sickle-celled anemia is different from that of normal humans. This disease has been described by Pauling as a "molecular disease." Ingram (1956, 1957), has shown that this difference results from the fact that valine replaces glutamic acid in the chain (see Fig. 69) and this, according to Ingram, is the only change present in the molecule. Crick says of this "it may surprise the reader that the alteration of one amino acid out of a total of about 300 can produce a molecule which (when homozygous) is usually lethal before adult life."

When the process of synthesis of proteins is studied, one particularly important problem has to be considered and that is how to explain the mechanism which controls the order of the amino acids in a protein. The condensation of amino acids into polypeptide chains is fairly simple to explain chemically but their order is not. This order must be very critically and stringently controlled since, as we have seen in the foregoing, the slightest variation in sequence of amino acids in the hemoglobin molecule can produce a lethal disease. Thus the critical point in protein synthesis is the joining up of the amino acids in a predetermined order. Now, it has been mentioned earlier in this discussion that nucleic acids are concerned with the synthesis of protein and it is almost certain that DNA has an important influence in deciding the sequence of amino acids.

That DNA can affect protein synthesis is demonstrated by the fact that when DNA is squirted by the T2 bacteriophages previously described into bacterial cells without any of the protein going in with it, it appears to be able to control the synthesis of protein inside the bacterium.

PERMEABILITY OF THE NUCLEAR MEMBRANE

If the nucleus is concerned with protein metabolism, we should say a word about the penetration of the nuclear membrane, because in animal and plant cells protein or some other substance must get out into the cytoplasm for the nucleus to exercise control over protein synthesis. We have mentioned before the effect which the existence of pores might have on the permeability of the nuclear membrane. Some direct permeability studies have been carried out and, while there is no intention here of trying to review this work, it may be pointed out that polypeptides and proteins seem to penetrate into the membrane readily. Conversely, dipeptidase and other enzymes have been shown to diffuse out readily from isolated nuclei. However, the permeability of the membrane in such cases may result from damage to the nuclei during the process of isolation. Brachet has described experiments in which both ribonuclease and deoxyribonuclease appear to penetrate the membrane of isolated nuclei and to cause an alteration in its shape. The same criticism which has just made could apply to his work, but Brachet anticipated this by demonstrating the penetration of ribonuclease (molecular weight 13,000) into the nuclei in intact amoebae (see Fig. 70) and onion tip cells. Protamines and histones also appear to penetrate readily into the nuclei of living cells and this process according to Fischer and Wagner requires energy since it is inhibited by dinitrophenol and cyanide. These few facts support the conception that the nuclear membrane serves only partly to isolate nuclear activity from that of the cytoplasm. Further information about the permeability of the nuclear membrane can be obtained from Brachet's book "Biochemical Cytology."

Up to the present we have been considering whether

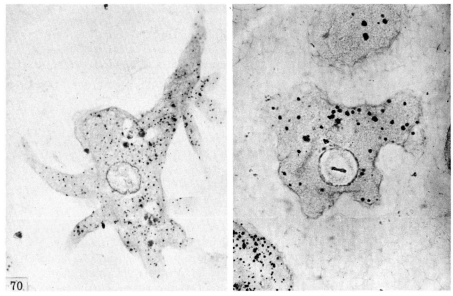

FIG. 70. *This illustration demonstrates that a protein (ribonuclease) can penetrate the cell membranes of living cells. Left, a normal* Amoeba *stained to demonstrate RNA. Right, RNA stain in another* Amoeba *which has been treated with ribonuclease. Note decrease in number of granules in* Amoeba *on right. (From Brachet, 1957, "Biochemical Cytology," Academic Press, New York.)*

protein is being synthesized only in the nucleus, we know that both DNA and RNA are present in the nucleus and that DNA exerts an effect on protein synthesis. Perhaps we should divert for a minute here to consider what is probably one of the most important pieces of evidence of the relationship of RNA to protein production. This is the work which has been carried out recently on tobacco mosaic virus by two groups, by the Gierer and Schramm (1956) group and by the group of Fraenkel Conrad. There are a number of strains of tobacco mosaic virus, and some of these strains have a protein which contains histidine. Gierer and Schramm showed that if you take the RNA part of the virus and free it completely from protein, it can still be infective although it is not as infective as when combined with protein. Fraenkel Conrad was able to recombine the protein and RNA of the virus and obtain again an active virus in which the infectivity was high but not quite normal. It is of interest that by swapping the RNA's and proteins from different strains it is possible to obtain different combinations. If, for instance, the virus, which is made by taking the RNA of one strain and the protein from another, is used to infect a tobacco plant, the virus which is reproduced in the plant is similar not to the virus from which the protein was taken but to the one from which the RNA was taken. So that, for example, if in the particular strain of virus from which the RNA was taken there was no histidine in the protein, then the virus removed from the tobacco plant after infection would also have no histidine; in other words, the RNA of the virus determines the composition of the protein of the virus. Furthermore the protein which was in the original virus was reproduced in the plant, and this protein was that of the virus from which the RNA originally came.

Let us return now, however, to the question of where in the cell is protein produced? There is RNA present in the nucleolus and RNA present in the form of small granules about 150 A in diameter associated with the endoplasmic reticulum. This endoplasmic reticulum, as has been described previously, breaks up on homogenization of the cell and is centrifuged down as microsomal particles. Crick makes the following comment: "Biologists should contrast the older concept of microsomes with the more recent and significant one of microsomal particles. Microsomes came in all sizes and were irregular in composition, microsomal particles occur in a few sizes only, have a fixed composition, and a much higher proportion of RNA. It is hard to identify microsomes in all cells whereas RNA-rich particles appear to occur in almost every kind of cell. In short, microsomes were rather a mess whereas microsomal particles appeal immediately to one's imagination and it will be surprising if they do not prove to be of fundamental importance."

SYNTHESIS OF PROTEIN BY NUCLEOLI

We shall first discuss briefly the case for the synthesis of protein by the nucleoli. It has already been mentioned that the nucleolus contains a good deal of RNA but it also contains some DNA and Caspersson claims it is rich in diamino acids. The presence of protein masked phospholipids has also been claimed, and alkaline glycerophosphatase and acid phosphatases have been demonstrated in this organelle by a number of authors, and also a great variety of other phosphatases by the present author. Other enzymes are present in the nucleolus, e.g., dipeptidase, cytochrome c reductase, nucleoside phosphorylase, and the DPN synthesizing enzyme; the two latter are present in a higher concentration in the nucleoli than in the cytoplasm. Many SS— and SH— groups are also present, and, in general, the nucleolus has from about 40 to 85% of dry matter, which is, relatively speaking, a very considerable amount. Although the nucleolus is an area in the nucleus where there is a large concentration of special substances, the electron microscope has to date given no evidence that it is surrounded by a limiting membrane. Originally Caspersson suggested that the nucleolus was the center of protein synthesis and part of this suggestion is due to the fact that the nucleolus is large and well developed in protein synthesizing cells and that in such cells it is particularly rich in RNA.

The conception that the nucleolus plays a part in protein metabolism has been made likely by the work of Ficq. She noted by tract autoradiography that glycine and phenylalanine containing radioactive carbon are incorporated more rapidly into the nucleoli than into the cytoplasm. In the case of oocytes which are growing rapidly and thus synthesizing much protein the rate is extremely fast. Similarly nucleic acid precursors are concentrated from 100 to 1000 times faster in nucleoli of such eggs than in the cytoplasm.

Further mention should be made of the localization of alkaline phosphatase in nucleoli. This was first recorded by the present author in 1943 as a result of histochemical studies and was subsequently confirmed by a number of workers— since then the present author has described the remarkable dephosphorylating activity of the nucleoli for a wide variety of phosphate substrates. This is shown particularly by the Purkinje cells of the cerebellum and by other cells which produce appreciable amounts of protein. The nucleoli of these cells readily dephosphorylate glycerophosphate, numerous sugar phosphates, riboflavin-5-phosphate, pyridoxal phosphate, ethanolamine phosphate, various steroid phosphates, and a wide range of phosphate esters which are concerned with intermediary metabolism and particularly the high-energy phosphates. In cells which are actively producing protein, phosphatase is not only present in the large nucleoli but in the cytoplasm of the cell as well. Bradfield, for example, showed that an active phosphatase is present in the cells of the silk spinning glands of insects which synthesize and secrete protein at an extraordinarily fast rate. Phosphatase is also present in the cells and fibers during proliferation of connective tissue after wounding. There is an increase in the enzyme in the fiber-producing cells at the time of fiber production. In periosteal fibrosarcomas where no bone is produced and also in polyostotic fibrous dysplasia, alkaline phosphatase is seen in both nucleoli and cytoplasm of the fiber-producing cells. Siffert has pointed out that the frequent association of alkaline phosphatase with the matrix of both fibers and cartilage would indicate an association with matrix production. It is of interest that phosphatases are present in the uterus of the hen and the mantle edge (which secretes the shell) of mollusks. Both the uterus and the mantle edge produce considerable amounts of protein. The egg shell of the hen has no calcium phosphate in it, and the shell of the mollusk has only very small amounts of phosphate so that it seems in these cases the enzyme is more concerned with matrix production, in other words with protein synthesis than with mineralization; the enzyme is also present particularly in regions where histogenesis is occurring. Jeener has shown that alkaline phosphatases are associated with cell proliferation in organs stimulated by sex hormones. Some phosphatases are also present in other parts of the nucleus but their significance will not be discussed here.

These facts together with the association of the enzymes with the nucleolus strongly support the concept of the importance of the latter in protein synthesis. It is of interest that here is a localized region of the nucleus without an obvious membrane in which, presumably, the protein metabolism of the nucleus is centered. Although the nucleolus is itself separated from the cytoplasm by the surrounding nuclear elements, as mentioned earlier, it is mobile and able to make direct physical contact with the nuclear membrane on occasions. It is possible, that on these occasions the nucleolus may discharge its protein through the nuclear membrane. Whatever the role of the nucleolus in protein synthesis, we must accept the conception that a substantial amount of protein synthesis also takes place in the cytoplasm.

Cytoplasmic localization of RNA provides some evidence for this. The recent work of Barrows and Chow on the intracellular distribution of vitamin B_{12} adds support to it. Vitamin B_{12} is associated with protein synthesis possibly through the formation of RNA, but RNA *and* DNA are decreased in vitamin B_{12} deficiency, and the incorporation of P^{32} into nucleic acids is effected in this condition. The distribution of vitamin B_{12} in homogenates of the liver is 40% in the microsomes, 13% in the mitochondria, and 11% in the nuclei, with 22% in the supernatant. Although only 11% of vitamin B_{12} is present in the nuclei, if this were all localized in the nucleolus it would represent an appreciable concentration in this region.

It is of interest in view of what has just been said about the nucleolus that protein synthesis can, in fact, take place in the cytoplasm even in the absence of the nucleus. It appears that the RNA particles which are associated with the endoplasmic reticulum are the center of such activity and it is noteworthy that in the synthesis of protein the amino acids have been said to "flow" through these particles. The first experiments on this subject were those by Zamecnik *et al.* (1956). They showed that if rats were given fairly large quantities of radioactive amino acids, later, after the animal was killed and liver homogenates prepared, the microsomal particles (the endoplasmic reticulum) contained a constant amount of this particular amino acid indicating that they were fixed by this part of the cell. However, in the second experiment a very small amount of radioactive amino acid was administered, and, in this instance within a short time, the radioactivity present in the microsomes rose steeply and then fell away quite quickly. This is obviously what one would expect if the protein in these particles was turning over very rapidly. Whether this in fact means that the amino acids are adsorbed onto the microsomes,* converted into proteins, and then passed out of the microsomes again as protein one cannot say but this is a distinct possibility.

There seems to be some evidence now that the amino acids have to be activated before they can be condensed into proteins and this activation requires the presence of ATP. An amino acid-activating enzyme has now been discovered and found to be widely distributed and is believed to be present in all cells which undertake the synthesis of protein. Following the activation of amino acids, the next step in protein production appears to be the transfer of the amino acids at least in the cytoplasm to the RNA particles of the endoplasmic reticulum by what appears to be a covalent bond. If the amino acids are labeled

---

* When the term microsomes is used it should be assumed that reference is being made to the RNP particles of the endoplasmic reticulum unless otherwise stated.

with radioactive atoms, then the RNA becomes labeled and can be extracted from the solution, purified, and then added to the microsomal fraction of a homogenate. The labeled amino acid is then transferred from the RNA to the protein of the microsome. This is an extremely interesting step in the problem of protein synthesis. It is also of interest that RNA can be synthesized without protein necessarily being synthesized at the same time. Normally one finds that in a cell which is undergoing active RNA synthesis, active protein synthesis is taking place at the same time. However, the synthesis of protein in such a system can be brought to a full stop by the use of chloramphenicols, this is particularly well shown in systems obtained from bacteria. However, if the protein synthesis is stopped in this way by chloramphenicol, synthesis of RNA continues unaffected. In the synthesis of protein by certain bacteria, e.g, *Escherichia coli* (Gross and Gross, 1956) there are some mutants of this organism which require a specific amino acid. If this amino acid is not supplied then the synthesis of both protein and RNA comes to a stop. If the chloramphenicol is given nothing further happens but, if in the next stage a small amount of the required amino acid is added, then RNA synthesis starts up very rapidly without affecting the protein synthesis. Then, if the chloramphenicol is removed from the system, protein synthesis will start again and proceed very rapidly. Crick in his article in 1958, points out that the concepts of protein synthesis include two important points. (1) The specificity of a nucleic acid is expressed solely by the sequence of its bases and this sequence is a simple code for the amino acid sequence of a particular protein in which the nucleic acid is concerned in synthesis. (2) Information once passed into a protein cannot get out again (the central dogma). In other words, the transfer of information from nucleic acid to nucleic acid or from nucleic acid to protein may be possible. (By information we mean here the sequence of nucleotides in the case of nucleic acid, and of amino acids in the case of proteins.) However, the transfer of information in reverse, that is, the sequence of units from protein to nucleic acid or from protein to protein is impossible. Not everybody agrees with this suggestion and further information is required about it.

One should also mention that an appreciable amount of RNA is present in mitochondria and it is possible that mitochondria are capable of synthesizing protein. Studies in the author's laboratory by Sheridan have already been mentioned in which it was found that, in the liver cells of guinea pigs which were subjected to scurvy, the mitochondria were surrounded by layers and layers of ergastoplasmic reticulum or membranes, almost as if these were being synthesized on the surface of the mitochondria. In fact they are so closely applied to the surface of the mitochondria in some cases that it is very difficult to distinguish them from the mitochondrial membrane. Whether this means, in fact, that there is synthesis of this membrane going on or whether it means that the membrane has become closely apposed to the mitochondria, because the energy derived from mitochondria is required in the process of protein synthesis as carried out by the endoplasmic reticulum, one cannot tell. There is also a possibility that, since in scurvy protein synthesis is depressed, the mitochondria may be synthesizing additional endoplasmic reticular membranes in an attempt to compensate for the depressing effects of the vitamin C deficiency. Mitochondria are enormously increased in numbers in scurvy and also in plain starvation.

It is of interest that the RNA particles of the endoplasmic reticulum like those of the nucleoli measure approximately 150 A across, and hence uniformity of size as well as uniformity of structure may play a part in protein synthesis. We have already mentioned that the synthesis of RNA which itself determines synthesis of protein is probably under the control of the DNA, i.e., by the nucleus. This we know, for example, because a Mendelian gene controls the sequence of amino acids in human hemoglobin as shown by the work on sickle cell anemia and furthermore, spermatozoa transfer only DNA and no RNA.

What is the significance of the protein part of the RNA particle we do not know, presumably it is structural though it may be enzymic in nature. Thus, at the moment we can only agree with Crick's comment "the RNA forms the template and the protein supports and protects the RNA." Crick has suggested that the ribonucleoprotein particle is an open structure like a sponge and possibly molecules of appropriate size can diffuse in and out of it, however, the whole relationship of RNA to the protein in these particles requires further study.

The really critical problem in protein synthesis is actually, since there are only four bases in the nucleotides, what arrangement of four bases in the RNA molecule could determine the sequence of twenty amino acids in the synthesis of a protein. This problem is described as the "coding problem" and is one in which the next steps in our understanding of protein synthesis might be taken. There is very little experimental work in this direction as yet and most of the discussion has been hypothetical.

NUCLEOCYTOPLASMIC RELATIONSHIPS

This leads us on to the problem of the relationship between the nucleus and the cytoplasm and their mutual interreactions. In the first place we should consider such reactions in unicellular organisms. Full details of this subject should be obtained by reading Brachet's "Biochemical Cytology." Only a summary of these very interesting facts can be given here.

We know that the nucleus is largely composed of DNA, RNA, histone, and a number of proteins. The RNA is concentrated exclusively in the nucleoli and is very labile metabolically, and this is one of the reasons why it has been suggested that nucleolar RNA may be the source of the RNA of the cytoplasm. However, there are reasons to believe that, although it may contribute some part of the cytoplasmic RNA, which would be in agreement with Caspersson's observations, it does not contribute all of it and that the cytoplasm itself is the site of an appreciable syn-

see author note before preface

thesis. Both histochemically and biochemically it has been demonstrated that nuclei contain extremely little of the oxidative enzymes (cytochrome oxidase and succinic dehydrogenase) which are so characteristic of mitochondria. So that presumably the chemical events which take place in the nucleus are those which are predominantly anaerobic in nature. Nuclei contain glycolytic enzymes and also an enzyme which synthesizes DPN, using nicotinamide, nucleotide, and ATP. There are also present a number of enzymes which are concerned in purine and nucleoside metabolism. These occur in greater quantity in the nucleus than in the cytoplasm, at least as far as liver cells are concerned. It has been suggested by various authors, including Brachet, that these findings are in agreement with the fact that the nucleus could be the site of nucleotide, coenzyme, and nucleic acid synthesis. Many of the experiments which have endeavored to show some relationship between the various cellular components have been carried out on homogenates or by mixing of, say, nuclear fractions and mitochondrial fractions and so on, but these are likely to give a very misleading idea of what in fact does happen in the living cell. How important this is, is demonstrated by very interesting experiments carried out by de Fonbrune in 1939. He transplanted nuclei from one amoeba to another and showed that the nuclei control the characteristic streaming of the cytoplasm in each case so that the type of streaming of the cytoplasm of one amoeba is transferred to another species of Amoeba when the nucleus of the first cell is pushed into the second. The point of these experiments however, is that in the process of transfer the cell walls of the two amoebae must be in extremely close contact with each other and the nuclei are then simply pushed through the two cytoplasmic walls by means of a blunt glass probe. If, however, the nucleus is pushed out into the medium and then grafted back into the cell by pushing into the other cell, it loses its ability to divide and, in fact, many of its activities seem to stop. So one can only guess at what happens to the nuclei and mitochondria and possibly other parts of the cells when the latter is homogenized, washed in sucrose, spun down in centrifuges, drawn up in pipettes, squirted out of the pipettes, mixed up with various reagents, and so on. It is pretty certain that the cell organelles being used in this way are in a different state from those that exist in the living cell. It is interesting that Cutter (1955), and his colleagues have demonstrated that coconut milk contains a number of nuclei which swim freely in it and which presumably come from the endosperm cells. These nuclei, which are in a physiological liquid that the coconut supplies, are still not capable of mitosis and are capable only of degenerative division when they are transplanted back into endosperm cells.

Studies have been carried out on the Amoeba and on the unicellular alga, *Acetabularia,* which involve sectioning the cytoplasm so that one-half contains a nucleus and the other does not. The groups of workers concerned with these studies are Hammerling and his colleagues, Mazia, and Danielli and co-workers. See articles by J. Brachet, J. Hammerling and colleagues, J. F. Danielli and colleagues and other workers in "The relationship between nucleus and cytoplasm" (Exptl. Cell. Research, Supplement 6, 1959). If the nucleus is removed from an amoeba, the animal quickly loses its motility and ceases to put out pseudopodia, rounds up, and becomes spherical. It is of interest, however, that if the nucleus is removed from ciliates, the part which has no nucleus still retains ciliary action. It cannot engulf living organisms but, if both the nucleate half of the amoeba and the non-nucleate half are kept starving, the nucleate half dies within about three weeks and the half without a nucleus in two weeks so that is about 50% longer survival resulting, presumably, from the presence of the nucleus. If the nucleus is grafted into a fragment of cytoplasm of the amoeba that has no nucleus and if the animal has only been in this condition for two or three days, then there is a very dramatic reintroduction of pseudopod formation and characteristic amoeboid motility. However, if the half has been without a nucleus for about a week or longer then the introduction of a nucleus does not have the same rejuvenating effect, and it is apparent that irreversible changes have taken place in the cytoplasm.

Danielli has expressed the opinion that particularly in these amoebae and possibly in cells of higher animals the nucleus is responsible for the *type* of macromolecules which are produced whereas the cytoplasm plays the part of organization of these macromolecules into what he describes as functional units. On the other hand, there are probably also mutual interreactions between the cytoplasm and the nucleus; it is not just all one-way control.

Hammerling has carried out a number of extremely interesting experiments on *Acetabularia* (see Fig. 71 for diagram of structure of this alga), and we will take this

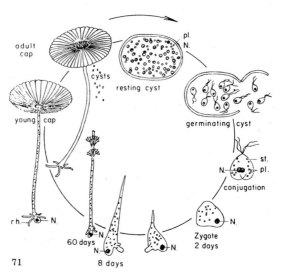

Fig. 71. *Life cycle of* Acetabularia mediterranea. (*From Brachet, "Biochemical Cytology," 1957, Academic Press, New York.*)

opportunity of referring hére to some of them. *Acetabularia,* a unicellular alga, normally has a stalk which contains some chloroplasts and a series of rhizoids, and in one of the larger rhizoids the nucleus is situated. At an appropriate period, the stalk forms a cap, which looks rather like that of a mushroom, and produces cysts which germinate and undergo a sexual union to form a zygote that reproduces the stalk and the rhizoids again. If a second rhizoid containing a nucleus is grafted onto the stalk of an acetabularian, it will form two of these caps instead of one. Here is an example of the effect of the nucleus on the cytoplasm. In the reverse experiment, Hammerling showed that, if a cap is removed from the acetabularia just before the nucleus goes into division, then nuclear division will stop and will not occur until a new cap has been formed. Presumably something necessary for the nucleus to divide is secreted by the cap, and, if the cap is continually removed, the process of mitosis can be delayed indefinitely. On the other hand, if the nucleate part of a rhizoid is grafted onto a plant which already has a nucleus, then a cap nuclear division can be produced within two weeks instead of what would be the normal time of about two months. In *Spirogyra* it was shown 50 years ago that, if the nucleus is removed, the non-nuclear parts of the cell survived for quite a long time, carried out photosynthesis, formation of plastids and fats, and production of tannic acid; the protoplasm continued to stream and there was even an increase in length. Thus a good deal of activity can go on in the cytoplasm even without the nucleus and yet in the end the cell processes do stop and the cell cannot continue to survive. True regeneration cannot occur without the presence of a nucleus.

Loeb in 1899 originally thought that the function of the nucleus was that of a center for cell oxidations but the fact that the nucleus contains practically no oxidative enzymes by biochemical studies and gives little or no reaction for these histochemically is evidence that this suggestion is not correct.

It is an interesting fact, in view of what has been said of the synthesis of coenzymes a little earlier, that, in 1925, E. B. Wilson had stated that the nucleus might be a storehouse of enzymes or of substances that activated cytoplasmic enzymes and that these substances may be concerned with synthesis as well as with destructive processes. It was suggested also, in 1892, by Verworn that the nucleus was the main synthetic center of the cell. This suggestion was also supported by Caspersson in the light of his various studies and he thought that the nucleus was the principal center for protein formation in the cell. Mazia in 1952 suggested that the function of the nucleus is really that of a replacement of products of cell activities and in support of this he points out that removal of the nucleus is not followed by effects which take place immediately but instead they take place over a period of time. For example, the nucleus produces enzymes, if the nucleus is removed then the cytoplasm will continue to function with the enzymes it has until they drop below a functional level—this may take place at different rates for different enzymes. Mazia has also suggested that as an alternative the nucleus might produce what could be described as a cytoplasmic unit which would be comparable to a plasmagene. It would play a part in cytoplasmic synthesis and would have to be replaced all the time by the nucleus if the cytoplasm was to be maintained normally. As soon as these cytoplasmic units were exhausted then the cytoplasm would not carry on its normal activities. Thus, although the nucleus may not be the center of oxidative processes in the cell, it may influence these processes and we should consider the evidence for and against this.

Figure 72 demonstrates the influence of the nucleus over RNA production.

Shapiro in 1935 by the process of micrurgy cut sea urchin eggs into two pieces, one half contained the nucleus and one did not, and he found that the oxygen consumption was much higher in the fragment which contained no nucleus. This is as one would expect from our knowledge that the cytoplasm contains mitochondria and that the mitochondria contain most of the respiratory enzymes of the cell. Brachet has also studied the oxidative processes in *Amoeba proteus* (1955) and he found that the removal of a nucleus had very little effect on the rate of respiration and, in fact, there was no change for at least seven days, but after that time the cytoplasmic fragments began to undergo cytolysis and the respiratory rate then fell off. The drop in the latter is understandable since the maintenance of the proper structural organization of the mitochondria and probably the related cytoplasm is necessary for the respiratory rate to be maintained. In the case of *Acetabularia* a similar result has been obtained, however, some studies which were carried out by Whiteley (1956) on the protozoan, *Stentor,* are of interest in this connection. He too severed his protozoan into two portions, one of which contained the nu-

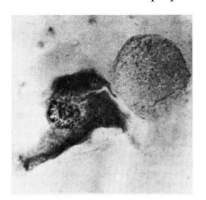

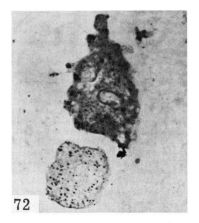

FIG. 72. *Two amoebae with severed portions. Note that anucleate portions show loss of basophilia, i.e., loss of RNA. (From Brachet, "Biochemical Cytology," 1957, Academic Press, New York.)*

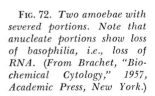

cleus and one did not and showed that in the fragment without a nucleus there was a drop in the consumption of oxygen and no regeneration, however, in the fragments which had a nucleus, regeneration occurred after 24 hrs. and there was a corresponding increase in O_2 consumption during this period. Eventually the respiratory rate came back to normal.

These results suggest that the macronucleus has some control, perhaps not over the actual respiration but over the synthesis of fresh respiratory equipment, in other words, of fresh mitochondria. The results with the amoebae and with *Acetabularia,* as Brachet says, completely invalidate Loeb's older conception that the nucleus was the center of oxidation processes in the cell. In fact, it is quite striking that the oxygen uptake is unaffected for quite a long time after the nucleus is removed from cells—in the case of the amoeba this is as long as ten days, in the case of *Acetabularia* as long as three months—and one cannot conclude from this that the nucleus once it has formed respiratory machinery exerts any significant control over its functioning. On the contrary, it appears that the nucleus is extremely dependent on the cytoplasm, and we have noticed a little earlier how important it is for the nucleus to be kept in contact with cytoplasm. Its removal from cytoplasm for even a short time renders it impossible for it to carry on its processes of division.

A relationship between the nucleus and cytoplasmic components is suggested by the results of tissue culture workers who have frequently described the migration of mitochondria within the cytoplasm of the cell so that they come into contact with the nuclear membrane, remain there for some time and finally disengage themselves. The nucleolus has often been observed to move through the nucleus and touch the nuclear membrane on the inside. It has been mentioned that usually it is met there by a mitochondrion. The cyclic movements of nucleolus and mitochondria in spinal ganglion cells noted by Tewari and the present author have also been already mentioned. In these cases it is possible that the nucleolus is discharging RNA or DPN through the nuclear membrane or, in the case where the mitochondrion is associated with the cell membrane, ATP is perhaps passed inward to the nucleolus.

Although the nucleus does not appear to have any special relationship to respiratory activity in the cytoplasm, it does have other effects of a quite fundamental nature. This has been very well demonstrated by experiments which have been carried out on amoebae by Brachet and his colleagues and which have given extremely interesting results. They showed that if amoebae are cut into nucleate and non nucleate parts, although the oxygen consumption is not significantly affected by this process, there is a disappearance of the ability to utilize glycogen in the nonnucleate part. In other words, the glycogen stores are scarcely affected (see Fig. 73), but, on the other hand, the protein tends to be

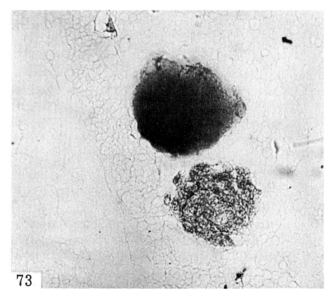

73

FIG. 73. *Two halves of amoebae. Dark glycogen staining of lower (anucleate) portion indicates failure to metabolize glycogen. (From Brachet, 1957, "Biochemical Cytology," Academic Press, New York.)*

used up so that the nucleus appears to control the process of glycogenolysis and also maintains the integrity of the protein of the cell. It is of interest that it takes a period of about 3 days before the carbohydrate breakdown stops and protein catabolism becomes increased. It is obvious, therefore, that the nucleus exercises very profound control over fundamental processes in the metabolism of the cytoplasm. Although there is a lag period before changes in the glycolytic system and protein metabolism occur in the nonnucleate part of the amoeba, changes in phosphate metabolism take place almost instantaneously. It was originally demonstrated by Mazia and Hirschfield in 1950 that the uptake of radioactive phosphate by the nonnucleated part of the amoeba was substantially less than that of the part containing the nucleus. Brachet and his colleagues repeated this experiment, first they placed whole amoebae in radioactive phosphate for some time and then separated the amoebae into nucleated and nonnucleated parts and demonstrated that there was no particular uptake of the radiophosphorus in the nucleated part as compared with the nonnucleated part. Then they presectioned amoebae and put the sectioned portions, nonnucleated and nucleated, into the radiophosphate and demonstrated that there was a rapid uptake of radioactive phosphorus in the nucleated portion and a great reduction of uptake in the nonnucleated portion, and, in fact, after a period of about 6 days there was 30 times more radioactive phosphorus in the former portion. This indicates, therefore, that the phosphate metabolism is profoundly affected in the absence of the nucleus. This result suggests that possibly the synthesis of ATP is affected in the half without the nucleus. However, it was demonstrated by Brachet that the nonnucleated part actually had more ATP and not less. On the other hand, what might be happening here is that the utilization of ATP has been reduced or greatly slowed down in the nonnucleated portion compared with the nucleated portion. This is particularly likely in view of the fact that phosphate uptake is reduced in the absence of a nucleus. This reduction brings us to the very interesting conclusion that we are dealing here with a situation in which the nucleus is responsible for the coupling of respiratory activity with oxidative phosphorylation, and it is quite possible, therefore, that when the nucleus is removed respiration is uncoupled from oxidative phosphorylation and this latter process comes to a dead stop even though the respiratory activity is unaffected. How the nucleus performs this function, whether it is by the production of a coenzyme, as Brachet has suggested, or not is difficult to say. A number of explanations have been put forward of this effect, but one of the most plausible is that, since by far the greater percentage of the DPN synthesizing enzyme is present in the nucleus, its removal deprives the cytoplasm of most of this critical coenzyme. Brachet makes this point too in his discussion of the problem. It was Hogeboom and Schneider who showed in 1952 that the DPN synthesizing enzyme is concentrated largely in the nuclei of liver cells and that the nuclei themselves contain considerable quantities of DPN. It has also been found to be present in fairly high concentrations in the *nucleoli* of the eggs of starfish. Since the nucleus controls the production of DPN, it is obvious that there would be a drop in DPN in the fraction of cytoplasm in which it is not present. Now DPN is essential for glycogenolysis and this would explain the holdup in this process in nonnucleated fragments. DPN, however, is also required for respiration, but the DPN concerned with respiration is not present in the cytoplasm but is conserved in the mitochondria and could conceivably not be affected by the process of removal of the nucleus. The DPN which is present in the cytoplasm and which is concerned with glycogenolysis might well be susceptible to breakdown by DPNases in the absence of a nucleus. The failure of production of more DPN by the nucleus and the extrusion by the former into the cytoplasm would be responsible for this chain of reactions grinding to a stop. Attempts to prove this hypothesis, which was enunciated by Brachet, were made by two authors, one of whom found that the DPN content in the nonnucleated portion of an amoeba decreased by more than half in a period of 75 hrs. after enucleation; the other author reported no change in the DPN level for 6 days. As Brachet says one will need to wait until this conflict is resolved before it is possible to assert or confirm this theory of the relationship of the nucleus to cytoplasmic respiration and oxidative phosphorylation.

When similar experiments are carried out on *Acetabularia*, the story does not seem quite the same. There appears to be very little difference in uptake of radiophosphorus between *Acetabularia* with nucleus or without nucleus. However, the situation is complicated by the fact that this alga carries out the process of photosynthesis and that photosynthetic processes are unaffected by the removal of the nucleus, and in fact the uptake of radioactive phosphate is concerned with photosynthesis. With *Acetabularia* it appears then that the nucleus does not exercise the same control as in animal cells.

One of the things that happens when an amoeba is enucleated is that the cytoplasm changes from a fibrillar appearance under the microscope to a granular one. At the same time the basophilia decreases in the nonnucleated portion and continues to decrease for some days after the removal of the nucleus. By the fifth day there is practically no basophilia in the fragment that does not contain the nucleus. All this suggests that there is breakdown of the endoplasmic reticulum, especially the ergastoplasmic part; the loss of basophilia presumably means loss of the RNA particles which were associated with these membranes (see Fig. 72). Whether this is in fact the proper interpretation of these changes, however, remains to be investigated with the aid of electron microscopy which is only now beginning to be applied to this particular problem. If this proves to be so, however, we have an example of another control exerted by the nucleus on the cytoplasm, that is, the maintenance of the cytoplasmic fine structure and particularly the content of RNA present in the cytoplasm. We have discussed earlier the possibility that the nucleus may produce RNA and pass it into the cytoplasm of the cell.

A very ingenious and interesting experiment was conducted by Goldstein and Plaut in 1955 and described by Brachet. These two authors cultivated organisms known as *Tetrahymena* which they had immersed in radioactive phosphate solution and the amoebae were then permitted to feed on them. Presumably then the radioactive phosphorus which was liberated into the cytoplasm of the amoebae was absorbed into the nucleus and possibly converted into RNA. After the digestion of the *Tetrahymena,* the nucleus from an amoeba which had ingested these radioactive animals was then grafted either into an amoeba which already had a nucleus or into an enucleated amoeba. In the case of the latter, within a relatively short period of time, 12 hrs. or so, radioactive RNA was found to be present in the cytoplasm. That this was RNA was demonstrated by the fact that, after treatment of this organism with ribonuclease, no radioactive particles could be shown by autoradiographic techniques to be present in the cytoplasm.

Another point of interest is that where such a nucleus was poked into an amoeba which already had its own nucleus, radioactive particles of RNA soon appeared in the cytoplasm but these particles did not pass back into the original nucleus which remained free of radioactivity during the whole of the experiment. This indicates that the passage of RNA is probably one-way only, that is, from the nucleus into the cytoplasm.

Brachet has pointed out, however, that Goldstein and Plaut have themselves made the point that the radioactive material which is discharged from the nucleus into the cytoplasm is not necessarily RNA that has been formed in the nucleus. It may, in fact, be a precursor or it may be that the radioactive phosphate is taken up in the nucleus and passed back into the cytoplasm as such and then syn-

thesized as RNA in the cytoplasm itself. However, even if
this is so, it is of interest that the nucleus is a source of
phosphate which is used for RNA synthesis in the cytoplasm
or a source of a precursor which is used for this purpose.
It should be mentioned that Goldstein and Plaut made the
point that their findings do not suggest that synthesis of
RNA in the cytoplasm as such is excluded. All they have,
in fact, demonstrated is that RNA or else some precursor or
radioactive phosphate is passed from the nucleus into the
cytoplasm so that *some* of the RNA in the cytoplasm may
be derived from this nuclear source. However, in this connection one point which should be remembered is that, in
the nonnucleated parts of the amoeba, there is a great drop
in RNA following the removal of the nucleus which suggests that a good deal of the cytoplasmic RNA is nuclear in
origin. However, it is possible that cytoplasmic synthesis of
RNA may be under control of the nucleus by means of a
coenzyme, so these experiments are not yet quite conclusive.
Brachet makes the point that, if the RNA metabolism is
affected in the enucleated amoeba, there should be some
inhibition in the synthesis of protein since there are many
pieces of evidence which link these two processes together
as has been described earlier. Mazia and Prescott in 1955
found that the amount of methionine labeled with radioactive sulfur (S^{35}) which is incorporated into a nonnucleated
Amoeba fragment is two and a half times less than the
amount incorporated in the fragment with the nucleus.
This difference however does not occur until 3 days after
the amoeba has been severed in two. This provides some
evidence that there is a link between protein synthesis and
RNA synthesis and that in this indirect way, by control
over the cytoplasmic RNA, the nucleus also controls the
protein synthesis in the cell. It should be noted that
protein synthesis does not fall to zero in fragments without
a nucleus, so there is a residual cytoplasmic synthesis of
proteins which persists even although the nucleus is removed from the cytoplasm.

It is not known whether the nucleus controls the synthesis of all the different types of cytoplasmic proteins. Brachet has studied changes in a number of different enzymes in the nonnucleate halves of amoebae and has demonstrated that various types of enzymes are affected in different ways by the nucleus. (Enzymes are, of course, proteins so the study of the enzymes gives an indication of the synthesis of this particular type of protein.) Protease, enolase, and adenosine triphosphatase are enzymes which appear to undergo very little or no change once the nucleus is removed. Amylase, on the other hand, seems to increase slightly in activity then drops back to normal level so that it is not affected very much. Dipeptidase decreases in the beginning and then remains at a constant lower level whereas acid phosphatase and esterase are reduced progressively and after a few days cannot be demonstrated as being present at all. Thus different enzymes are obviously under nuclear control to different degrees, and it becomes obvious that control of the nucleus over cytoplasmic proteins is a very complex one.

It has been suggested by Brachet that the difference in behavior of the enzymes might be related to their localization in the cell. He points out that Holter in 1955 demonstrated that amylase and protease were incorporated in very large granules which were either mitochondrial or were possibly the lysosomes of De Duve which we have described earlier. This might suggest, as earlier evidence has possibly demonstrated, that the mitochondria do not appear to be under the control of the nucleus. Dipeptidase is in the cytoplasm proper and is not bound to the mitochondria so one could understand that it might be reduced in the absence of the nucleus. Acid phosphatase and esterase which decrease progressively when the nucleus is removed may possibly be bound to the microsomes (E.R.) as shown by Brachet. Some acid phosphatase seems to be associated with the mitochondria, and De Duve has claimed that acid phosphatase is one of the hydrolytic enzymes found in his lysosomes. We have no certainty that all the different types of hydrolytic enzymes are present in the one lysosome; it may be there are different lysosomes, some containing acid phosphatase, some containing cathepsin, and others proteases and so on, and if this is the case it is possible that some of these are affected by the absence of the nucleus and some are not.

It is also of interest that Danielli and his colleagues in 1955 made hybrid amoebae by putting the nucleus of one species into the cytoplasm of another and then prepared antibodies against the two species. They found that the lysis of the hybrid amoeba is under the control of the nucleus. This appears to demonstrate that the determination of antigenic specific characters, as Brachet puts it, is under the "nuclear dominance while the morphological and physiological character of the hybrid is under cytoplasmic dominancy." It is of interest that in our earlier discussions in this book on the role of the nucleolus on the synthesis of RNA we mentioned that the dissected out nucleoli of *Acetabularia* exposed to radioactive phosphate had incorporated P^{32} with extraordinary rapidity into their RNA so this is a very good support of the claim that the nucleolus is a center of RNA synthesis since it contains nearly all the RNA of the nucleus. It is of interest that in the case of *Acetabularia* the removal of the nucleus actually stimulates RNA synthesis in the cytoplasm, but it is also to be noted that in intact *Acetabularia* the nucleolus is much more active than the cytoplasm in the production of RNA. It has been suggested by Brachet that this can be explained by the fact that the high activity of the nucleolus in production of RNA in intact *Acetabularia* is due to the fact that the precursors of RNA are snatched away from the cytoplasm before they can be used there for its synthesis. However, the mechanism for synthesis of RNA is present and active in the cytoplasm and the removal of the nucleus (with its contained nucleolus) removes competition for the precursors; the cytoplasm could then obtain all that was necessary. In the case of "protein synthesis" (absorption of labeled amino acids) in *Acetabularia,* it has been demonstrated that the amino acids appear in the nucleolus before they appear in the cytoplasm and that once the nucleus is removed, protein synthesis by the nonnucleated portion is actually faster than in the nucleated portion and this "ties in" well with the demonstrated increase of RNA synthesis. It also shows that the nucleus is not essential for the synthesis of protein by the cytoplasm, but further experiments have demonstrated that such anucleate protein synthesis is of a short-term nature (about three weeks) and that for it to be extended over a long period of time the nucleus is necessary. It is of interest that, although the synthesis comes to an end, the turnover (breakdown) of protein continues for quite a number of weeks even if the nucleus is not present.

A striking thing about the intact cell is the metabolic activity of the RNA contained in the nucleolus in comparison with that found in the cytoplasm. Some early work suggested that incorporation of precursors into RNA was faster in the nucleolus than in the cytoplasm, and there is now a good deal of evidence that this is so mostly from autoradiographic studies by Ficq in 1955. By working with the oocytes of echinoderms and amphibians, she demonstrated that radioactive labeled adenine and orotic acid were incorporated very rapidly into RNA in the nucleolus. In the lampbrush chromosomes of amphibian eggs, adenine could be found to be incorporated very rapidly into the loops of the chromosomes, which are known to contain RNA. There have also been some studies with radioactive phosphate and a number of authors have demonstrated that it too is preferentially absorbed into the nucleolus. All these findings, together with the previous literature, strongly support the conception that the nucleolus in particular is a very active site of synthesis of RNA and that it is the source of at least part of the cytoplasmic RNA.

The incorporation of labeled amino acids into the protein of the nucleus has been subject to some small controversy.

Originally it was believed that the rate of incorporation into the nucleus was no more rapid than into the cytoplasm, but this was probably due to the fact that the work was carried out on aqueous homogenates and that nuclei lose a certain amount of their protein in such homogenates. It was not until homogenates were studied by nonaqueous techniques that it was found that labeled amino acids were incorporated into nuclear proteins very rapidly. Brachet points out that the proteins of the nucleus are presumably either the constituents of the chromatin or they represent protein which is localized in the nucleolus, and it is not possible to tell for certain with the homogenate technique just where in the nucleus the proteins are localized.

Ficq and Brachet have demonstrated that in the liver cells of higher animals the nuclear proteins incorporate radioactive amino acids much more actively than cytoplasmic proteins but in the case of the nuclei of the pancreas, the intestine, the lung, heart, muscle, kidneys, spleen, and uterus this is not so.

In developing embryos it has been demonstrated that all the nuclei show a very much higher incorporation of radioactive amino acids than the cytoplasm and since, as Brachet points out, there is a considerable synthesis of proteins in the nucleus in actively dividing cells, this is just what would be expected.

The conclusons made by Brachet about this problem is that there is no doubt that the nucleus and particularly the nucleolus has a very active metabolism of RNA but that protein metabolism is not more active in the nucleus than it is in the cytoplasm, the exception being those cells which are undergoing rapid division. This is of interest in view of the fact that, since RNA is being made relatively more rapidly than proteins are being synthesized in the nucleus particularly in the nucleolus, more RNA is being formed than is necessary for this purpose. It seems likely, therefore, that the excess RNA passes to the cytoplasm.

Brachet has given a general discussion of the possible

relationships of the nucleus and the cytoplasm and the readers are referred to his book for full details. However, certain of the more essential conclusions might be repeated here. One of the functions which the nucleus could perform since it is relatively poor in enzymes is the production of coenzymes, and it is possible that some of the enzymes found in the cytoplasm might be under the regulation of the coenzymes secreted by the nucleus. The importance of coenzymes might explain the association of the mitochondria with the nuclear membrane which has been recorded by quite a number of authors. However, we only know for certain that DPN as a coenzyme is made by the nucleus and we do not know for certain what other enzymes might be produced by it. It is of interest that Tewari & Bourne have produced considerable evidence that the nucleolus in spinal ganglion neurones synthesize ATPase and glucose-6-phosphatase and passes it first to the body of the nucleus then to the cytoplasm. The striking effect, however, of this association is that the activities of the mitochondria seem to be pretty well independent of the nucleus in so far as cellular oxidation is concerned since the oxidation proceeds whether the nucleus is there or not. However, as we have pointed out earlier, it is an interesting possibility that the nucleus acts as a device for coupling by some means or other oxidative phosphorylation with respiration. The independence or otherwise of the mitochondria from the nucleus is of interest, and Brachet points out as we have done earlier in this discussion that the nucleus may in fact depend upon its supply of energy (ATP) from the mitochondria.

Where, however, the nucleus appears to exert its effect most strongly is on the endoplasmic reticulum, and, since it has been demonstrated that great decrease of basophilia and change in the nature of the cytoplasm occurs when the nucleus is removed from the *Amoeba,* it seems possible that the real relationship between the nucleus and the cell lies in the control by the former over the endoplasmic reticulum. Its control here may be dependent on

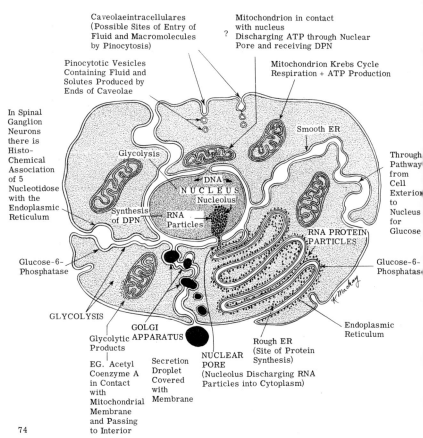

Caveolaeintracellulares
(Possible Sites of Entry of
Fluid and Macromolecules
by Pinocytosis)

Mitochondrion in contact
with nucleus
? Discharging ATP through Nuclear
Pore and receiving DPN

Pinocytotic Vesicles
Containing Fluid and
Solutes Produced by
Ends of Caveolae

Mitochondrion Krebs Cycle
Respiration + ATP Production

In Spinal
Ganglion
Neurons
there is
Histo-
Chemical
Association
of 5
Nucleotidose
with the
Endoplasmic
Reticulum

Glycolysis

Smooth ER

DNA
NUCLEUS
Nucleolus

Through
Pathway
from
Cell
Exterior
to
Nucleus
for
Glucose

Synthesis
of DPN

RNA
Particles

RNA PROTEIN
PARTICLES

Glucose-6-
Phosphatase

Glucose-6-
Phosphatase

GLYCOLYSIS

Endoplasmic
Reticulum

GOLGI
Glycolytic APPARATUS
Products
|
EG. Acetyl
Coenzyme A
in Contact
with
Mitochondrial
Membrane
and Passing
to Interior

Secretion
Droplet
Covered
with
Membrane

NUCLEAR
PORE
(Nucleolus Discharging RNA
Particles into Cytoplasm)

Rough ER
(Site of Protein
Synthesis)

74

FIG. 74. *Division of labor in cells. The cisternae of the E.R. are shown much wider than they are in most cells. The E.R. itself is also much more greatly convoluted in reality. It should be stressed, however, that this is purely a diagrammatic representation of a cell. (Drawing by K. Mackay.)*

the secretion of RNA granules which become attached to the reticulum. (See Fig. 74 for summary of division of labor in cells.)

Originally it was suggested by Caspersson that DNA was really the nucleic acid fundamentally concerned with the synthesis of complex proteins. More recently it has been suggested that DNA probably directly synthesizes the proteins of the chromosomes, in other words it causes a reproduction of the protein portion of the genes.

It is very likely that RNA plays an important part in embryological processes and it might be of interest in concluding this chapter to repeat Brachet's conception of its role. "Since the synthesis of proteins is primarily a cytoplasmic process and since, as we know, the RNA present in the ergastoplasmic small granules certainly plays a part in the synthesis, it is tempting to visualize the whole process in the following, entirely hypothetical way. Under the influence of the nuclear genes, specific cytoplasmic RNA's would be synthesized; these RNA's are probably not entirely synthesized in the nucleus, and it is possible that interactions between purely cytoplasmic RNA and RNA of nuclear origin occur. The specific RNA's would in turn organize the synthesis of specific cytoplasmic proteins according to the well-known template hypothesis."

CHAPTER VII

Specialized cells: gland cells, muscle fibers and nerve fibers.

UP TO DATE WE HAVE BEEN dealing with cells in a rather general way, using a variety of cell types to illustrate points concerning cell physiology. It is proposed now in the last stages of this book to consider two or three specific types of cells. To begin this chapter we will consider the glandular cell and, since there are a wide variety of both exocrine and endocrine glands in the body, comments will be restricted to the type of secretion process which is demonstrated particularly well either in the salivary glands or the pancreas and particularly we will refer to the pancreas, although some details of the salivary glands will be included as well.

The mechanism of secretion in externally secreting glands has been a subject of study for a good many years and very detailed work was published on this subject by Nassonow in 1923; Bowen in a series of publications between 1924 and 1929 fully confirmed and extended Nassonow's work. The general trend of studies by Nassonow and Bowen was the relationship of the Golgi material in particular to the production of secretion droplets. They both demonstrated that the first droplets of secretion which are visible under the optical microscope appeared in the interstices of the Golgi network, that as the number and size of these droplets increased, the Golgi network became hypertrophied and that when the cell carried its full load of secretion the apparatus appeared to break up and small pieces of it appeared to become attached to some of the secretory granules.

Studies have been made on the pancreatic cells of external secretion (as distinct from the islets of Langerhans) from the point of view of fine structure. The pancreatic cell structure can thus be taken as a general model for the cells of external secreting glands.

Two groups have made a special study of the fine structure of the acinar cells of the pancreas. These two are Ekholm and Edlund (1959) who investigated the human pancreas and Palade and Siekewitz (1958) who studied the guinea pig pancreas. Generally speaking there was little difference between the two types of pancreas. The same cytoplasmic elements—the endoplasmic reticulum with associated ribonucleoprotein granules, the mitochondria, and the zymogen granules were present in both.

In guinea pigs which had been starved, Siekewitz and Palade demonstrated that there was a well-formed endoplasmic reticulum (ergastoplasm) and that the cisternae (spaces between the pairs of membranes) were very small and had special orientation within the cell. There were very few granules in the cisternal spaces. The apical parts of the cell contained a number of zymogen granules and the lumina of the acini were very small and appeared to be occupied by an amorphous material which had a density similar to that of the zymogen granules. This finding agrees with the statement that secretion of zymogen does occur from the pancreas in small amounts even in long starvation. In guinea pigs that had been killed one hr. after feeding, there were many granules within the cisternae of the endoplasmic reticulum which were greatly distended. The number of zymogen granules found in the apex of the cell was generally less than in the starved animals. The lumina of the acini were distended and contained irregular and ill-defined masses of electron dense material which was probably discharged zymogen.

Siekewitz and Palade subsequently made a very interesting study of the functional variations in the microsomal fractions in the pancreas of the guinea pig. The microsomal fraction as mentioned before represents the endoplasmic reticulum plus its attached ribonucleic acid particles. Their experiments started from the fact that they observed that, when the microsomal fraction from starved guinea pigs was analyzed for enzyme activity, it was found that the ribonuclease and TAPase (trypsin activatable protease) activities varied a great deal in different preparations and in some cases reached as high as 30% of the activities found in the zymogen fraction. The zymogen fraction is that part of the homogenate of the pancreatic cells which is formed from the granules in the cell that are described as the zymogen granules and which are primarily comprised of digestive enzymes and precursors of enzymes— hence the name "zymogen." Since the zymogen fraction is composed almost exclusively of zymogen granules and since these have a higher total RNAase and TAPase activity than any of the other cell fractions, the authors wondered whether this similarity indicated some functional connection, and they initiated a series of experiments in order to test this out.

In other investigations they had found that in some cases dense granules had been found within the cisternae of the endoplasmic reticulum in electron microscope preparations of the exocrine cells of the pancreas of the guinea pig. These intracisternal granules could be compared, both from the point of view of fine texture which they demonstrated and their density, with the zymogen granules. However, there was a considerable difference in size and the zymogen granules appeared to be outside the endoplasmic reticulum whereas the smaller particles were actually in the cisternae between the double membranes. Further studies have demonstrated that these intracisternal granules are present in large numbers in this position about 1 and 2 hrs. after starved guinea pigs have been fed but that by 3 to 4 hrs.

they have more or less disappeared. The authors consider that, since it is the endoplasmic reticulum which forms the microsomes in homogenization, perhaps some of the high enzyme activity demonstrated in the microsomal fraction might have been due to the enclosure of some of these granules which were present within the microsomal cavity. They investigated this problem by taking various fractions from starved and fed animals, collecting the glands about 1 hr. after feeding, the time when they expected to obtain the highest concentration of granules within the cisternae of the endoplasmic reticulum. They were able to obtain subfractions an hour after feeding which consisted largely of cisternal granules together with some detritus derived from the microsomal fraction. They found that the TAPase and the RNAase activities present in this granular fraction were actually higher than those of the microsomes from which they were presumably derived and were sometimes as high as the values for the zymogen fraction as such. A similar increase in activity was also described for the enzyme amylase. The granules present in the cisternae were already in a finished state, and were probably destined therefore to become zymogen granules, but their precise position in the secretory circle is not clearly seen at the moment. It is known that in the late stages of the secretory cycle of the pancreas the large vacuoles in the Golgi zone become filled up with a material which has a high electron density, and it is possible that these intracisternal granules feed into the Golgi material and there condense into large granules which are passed to the apical part of the cell. Hirsch has said that in many cases it appears that the granules which are shed into the lumen of the pancreas appear to be enclosed in a structure resembling a membrane of cytoplasmic material. This might be explained in the following way. Assuming that there is a continuous passage from the endoplasmic reticulum lumen through the cisternae in the Golgi apparatus and so to the exterior, it is possible that Siekewitz and Palade's intracisternal granules

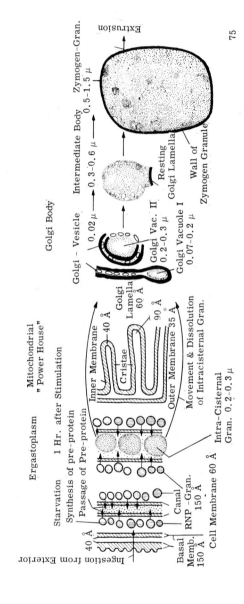

Fig. 75. *Hirsch's conception of "Production line" secretion by a cell. From Naturwissenschaften, 47, 25, 1960.*

pass to the Golgi apparatus and there coalesce to form large granules which then pass away from the Golgi material toward the apical part of the cell along those parts of the endoplasmic reticulum which lead to the exterior of the cell. Since these granules are very big when they leave the Golgi apparatus, they no doubt cause great dilation of the cisternae and it is even possible that as they are pushed out of the cell they tear part of the double membranes from the ergastoplasm and carry this as an investment as they pass out into the exterior. Even if there is no continuous passage it is quite possible that the droplets might be excreted from the cell covered with a submicroscopic skin derived from the endoplasmic reticulum or the Golgi membranes or simply composed of protein secreted on to them by one of these organelles.

Siekewitz and Palade point out that in their preparations, although they found a very high proteolytic RNAase activity in the isolated intracisternal granules, quite considerable proteolytic activity and RNAase activity were also found in the less dense fragments of the microsomes which presumably are composed simply of endoplasmic reticulum and the small RNA particles attached to them. It appears very likely that this activity is localized in the RNA protein particles. It is possible that these individual particles synthesize enzymes, become greatly enlarged, and pass through the membrane of the endoplasmic reticulum into the cisternae. The interrelation between cellular organelles according to Hirsch is shown in Figure 75.)

This represents a scheme for the production of secretion granules by the cell and the joint role of the endoplasmic reticulum, the mitochondria, and the Golgi apparatus in this process. According to this scheme, in the pancreas amino acids become associated with the RNA granules of the endoplasmic reticulum membrane (left of diagram) and are passed as preprotein (? polypeptides) into the cisternae where they grow in size to become the intracisternal granules of Palade and Siekewitz this stage is headed "1 hr. after stimulation" in the diagram).

In the text of this book the previous observations of Hirsch, in which he has seen "secretion" droplets in the pancreatic acinar cell moving through the cytoplasm to the Golgi zone have been mentioned, these droplets are approximately the same size as the intracisternal granules described by Palade and Siekewitz. Hirsch now believes that his moving droplets represent the intracisternal granules passing along the endoplasmic reticulum. The large secretion droplets of gland cells appear in the Golgi apparatus and if the intracisternal granules represent presecretory material their transference from the endoplasmic reticulum to the Golgi material requires some explanation. There is no evidence that the cisternae of the endoplasmic reticulum are continuous with the Golgi material but this possibility must be considered. Hirsch believes that the mitochondria provide the energy required to dissolve the cisternal granules, to pass them through the membranes of the endoplasmic reticulum and through the Golgi membranes inside which they become concentrated into droplets of secretion, growing larger and larger until they are converted into zymogen granules, surrounded by a membrane and pushed to apex of the cell ready for discharge. (Illustration from Hirsch "Die Naturwissenschaften" 2, 25, 1960.)

This is the morphological story to date as told by the electron and light microscopes. The metabolic story has been studied, using salivary gland material by Junquiera and his colleagues with rats as their experimental animals. Normal cats and rats with ligated salivary ducts were used. The significance of ligating the excretory duct is that it leads to cessation of secretion, disappearance of granules of secretion, decrease in size of the cells and the gland as a whole, and there is a corresponding decrease in activities of the enzymes. The gland does not undergo any degenerative process. Junquiera and his colleagues used these types of glands to study not only the histochemical and biochemical changes in the cells but they tried also to study the mor-

phological changes as demonstrated by the light microscope in an attempt to equate the various activities and
morphological elements in the cell with the processes
of secretion. These results are given in summary as follows. In the control gland it was found that there were
many mitochondria, they were mainly in the form of short
rods through some round specimens were present. As a result
of ligation they were very greatly reduced in numbers. Millon's histochemical test for proteins demonstrated a strong
reaction in the normally secreting gland and only a very
weak reaction in the gland which had been ligated. Studies
in basophilia (to demonstrate degree of accumulation of
RNA) showed a very strong basophilia in the control gland,
but in the ligated gland which was apparently not secreting
at all the basophilia was very weak. Biochemical investigation of the ratio of ribonucleoprotein over deoxyribonucleoprotein (RNAP/DNAP) showed this ratio to be 2.18 in cells
of the control gland but only 0.84 in the ligated gland, so
there was obviously a very profound decrease of RNA by
comparison with DNA in the nonsecreting gland. Biochemical studies of protease activity demonstrated that in the
control gland it was 560.0 μg. phenol/100 mg. tissue and in
the ligated gland it was 266.0 μg. phenol/100 mg. tissue. In
the mouse, the cathepsin activity was 16.9 μg. tyrosine/1 μg.
DNA protein and in the ligated gland it was not reduced
quite as much as some of the other enzymes but was down to
10.3 μg. tyrosine/1 μg. DNAP. Alkaline phosphatase varied
a little between rats and mice. In rats the figure was 2.8 mg.
phenol/100 mg. tissue and in the ligated gland it was 1.7 mg.
phenol/100 mg. tissue so this was a reduction of something
like a third. In mice curiously enough, in the control gland
there was 2.0 mg. phenol/100 mg. tissue of alkaline phosphatase and in the ligated gland it actually went up to 2.4
mg. phenol/100 mg. tissue. So it seems that if the alkaline
phosphatase is playing a significant part in the secretory
processes of rats, it is a specific process and it does not play
the same part in mice.

The acid phosphatase results were interesting because in rats the control gland showed 1.8 mg. phenol/100 mg. tissue activity and in the ligated glands there was no change at all. In mice, however, in the control gland there was 2.0 mg. phenol/100 mg. tissue activity and in the ligated gland 0.42 mg. phenol/100 mg. tissue, so that, perhaps, if phosphatase is playing a part in the secretory cycle, then in the rat it is alkaline phosphatase that is involved and acid phosphatase in the mouse.

Succinic dehydrogenase was studied by Thunberg's methylene blue method and there was found to be high activity (50% reduction in 12 min. of methylene blue) in the control gland and in the ligated gland there was a 12% reduction in color, which was decreased in mice to less than a quarter. There was not quite as much reduction in rats; using the Warburg apparatus there was a 63% increase of the QO_2 after the addition of succinate and in the ligated glands only 28% increase. So there was a significant reduction in oxidative activities which was confirmed by the cytochemical indophenol oxidase test for cytochrome oxidase, the control gland cells giving a dark blue and ligated glands only a light blue color with this reagent. The oxygen consumption in the rat cells gave a QO_2 of 4.2 in the control gland and only 1.8 in the ligated gland. The figure for glycolysis and the glycolytic quotient in relation to nitrogen was 3.2 in the control gland and 3.3 in the ligated gland, so there was significant different in the glycolytic rate. The ATP and ADP combined figure was 13.7 μg./1 μg. of DNA protein in the control gland and in the ligated gland it was only 3.2 μg./1 μg. of DNA protein. Creatine phosphorus was 8.5 μg./1 μg. DNAP * in the control gland and this was down to 2.7 μg./1 μg. DNAP in the ligated gland. Inorganic phosphorus dropped from 44.8 μg./1 μg. of DNAP in the control to 18.6 μg./1 μg. of DNAP in the ligated gland. Pyruvate utilization similarly dropped by about two-thirds and thus it appears from these figures that not only is there a drop

* DNAP = DNA phosphorus.

in respiratory activity of the cells when they are not secreting but there is also a drop, as one might expect, in oxidative phosphorylation. It is of interest, however, that glycolysis is maintained at a constant rate in both ligated and nonligated cells, and, as Junquiera and his colleagues point out, it appears that the energy derived from glycolysis itself is used by the cell largely for its basic needs and not for its specialized function as a secreting cell. It appears that the ATP, ADP, and phosphocreatine are really the compounds that are the sources of energy for the secretory process in the cell since there is such a spectacular decrease in these following ligation. It is of interest that the activity of cathepsin in the secretion of the salivary glands seems to be controlled *in vivo* by the male sex hormones. There is a parallel between cathepsin activity and protein synthesis, and the drop in activity of cathepsin in the cells of ligated glands may be significant from this point of view.

Junquiera and Hirsch have also described the light-microscope changes that take place in cells of ligated glands.

The Golgi apparatus is undoubtedly related to the processes of secretion if the early work which we have mentioned before can be taken at its face value. Junquiera and Hirsch summarized the evidence for the participation of Golgi material in the process of secretion as follows. The Golgi apparatus changes in size and structure very considerably during the secretory cycle. Droplets appear in the substance of the Golgi material and gradually appear to be transformed into secretory granules. This fact has been observed not only in fixed and stained preparations but also in the living pancreas, for instance, by Hirsch in 1932. In 1939 he suggested that the Golgi bodies are the sites in the cell where cytoplasmic products congregate and become formed into zymogen granules. There is no biochemical data, as has been pointed out both by the present author and by Hirsch, that the Golgi bodies are actually the site of protein synthesis since they contain no RNA and do not appear to contain oxidative enzymes or other enzymes concerned with energy production, although in some cells such as the absorptive cells of the gut they do contain phosphatase, ATPase (heat stable), alkaline phosphatase, acid phosphatase, and so on.

In 1954, Sjöstrand and Hanson demonstrated by ultrastructural studies that there was an intimate relationship between the Golgi vacuoles, the zymogen granules, the ground substance of the Golgi apparatus and the alpha cytomembranes (endoplasmic reticulum): "there are all transition stages observed between, on the one hand, bodies with a pronounced elongated form and with the most direct topographic relations to the Golgi membranes and Golgi granules embedded in the ground substance on the other. The impression when observing these pictures is that they show snapshots of the conversion of membranes into granules and vice versa. The small granules seem to coalesce to bigger granules which gradually gain the size, form and opacity of the zymogen granules." This work appears to confirm the conception of the Golgi material as a condensing or aggregating region of the cell and reminds one of the statement of Kirkman and Severinghaus in 1938. "A great deal of work strongly suggests that the Golgi apparatus neither synthesizes secretory substances nor is transformed directly into them but acts as a condensation membrane for the concentration, into droplets or granules, of products elaborated elsewhere and diffused into the cytoplasm. These elaborated products may be lipoids, yolk, bile constituents, enzymes, hormones or almost any other form of substance."

We do not know, of course, to what extent these synthetic processes are controlled by the mitochondria. There are papers in the literature suggesting that the mitochondria actually produce the zymogen granules in the pancreas, and it seems very likely that in parts of the endoplasmic reticulum the mitochondria come in very intimate contact with the nucleoprotein granules on the outside of the membrane and that they supply the energy for the synthetic processes taking place in these particles. At any rate the particles of enzyme protein that are produced pass into the spaces and presumably undergo some benefit from contact with the Golgi material and possibly even from contact with the nucleus. One could conceive of them as all passing into the cisternal space which surrounds the nucleus, but to what extent the metabolic activity of the nucleus might affect any enzyme protein passing through this space one cannot say for certain. Perhaps the passage of the granules to the Golgi region serves not only as a mechanism whereby the granules are aggregated to a large zymogen granule but possibly something is done to prepare the enzymes for activity upon secretion. Also one should consider the possibility that vitamin C, despite the known defects of localization in the technique, may occur, as the present author has claimed, in the Golgi apparatus at times of great synthetic activity and there is a possibility that in passing through into an area which is saturated with a reducing substance, oxidation of the contents of these granules prior to their excretion may be prevented.

So we can see a division of labor very clearly in the process of secretion in the gland cell but the interesting thing, as we have been emphasizing right through this book, is that we are not dealing with an isolated division of labor but an interdigitating division so that each job fits in very well with the job done by another part of the cell.

THE STRIATED MUSCLE FIBER

The muscle fiber is composed of four fundamental constituents: (1) the sarcolemma which is the equivalent of the cell membrane; (2) the fibrils which represent the structural elements responsible for contraction; (3) the sarcosomes which are really the mitochondria and which contribute the supply of energy for muscular contraction; and (4) the sarcoplasm which is the ground cytoplasmic substance in which the other structures of the muscle fiber are embedded. In addition, there is a specialized region of the fiber called the motor end-plate at the point where the motor nerve fiber makes junction with the sarcolemmal membrane and which is responsible for initiating the contraction of the fiber. For the moment we will discuss very briefly the structure of each of these elements and we will include the description of the structure of the caveolae introcellulares with an account of the structure of the sarcolemma.

Muscle fibers themselves have three main shapes. They may be cylindrical with ends which are conical, they may be spindle-shaped with extremities tapering off very finely, or they may be conical with one end long and attenuated and a broad base at the other. This depends, of course, on their position in the muscle itself. The first of these types of fibers usually runs the whole length of the muscle, the second type is usually situated within the main part or belly of the muscle, the third type is usually attached to a tendon at one end and the other end terminating somewhere in the interior of the muscle itself.

The shape of a transverse section of muscle is oval or spherical when it is fresh but it shrinks considerably following fixation, and one usually finds rather angular cross sections of the fibres. Voluntary muscle fibers vary from about $10–100\mu$ in diameter. Presumably this difference in size is associated in some way with the amount of work which the muscle has to perform. There are in any single muscle, fibers of many different diameters. Fibers vary very much in length and may in some cases extend only a few millimeters and in others, fibers in excess of 34 cm. in length have been seen.

Schwann in 1839 and Bowman in 1840 described a thin membrane which surrounded the voluntary muscle fiber. It was described by Schwann as the cell membrane of the fiber and this was later agreed to by Bowman. It can be demonstrated by placing a muscle fibre in fresh water or by causing a sudden coagulation of the contents which then contract. The membrane or sarcolemma, as demonstrated in this way, seems to be a pale, colorless and apparently, under the optical microscope, structureless membrane, and it is semipermeable since if placed in water it swells by imbibition and if subsequently placed in concentrated sugar solution this water is removed. It was thought to be about 0.1μ across and to have a slight infolding at each Z band. Others have shown that the sarcolemma is more complicated, i.e., under the electron microscope there are two dark osmiophilic lines separated by a light osmiophilic line which together are approximately 300 A across, each of the lines in this triple structure being about 100 A thick; also there is a thick layer of dense material about 500 A thick which extends inward from the inner of the dark lines of the membrane.

Under the light microscope the early workers had described the sarcolemmal membrane as being about 0.1μ thick which is in fact 1000 A. We will see that, if we add the 500-A thick complex to the three lines which themselves total about 300 A, we get a figure of about 800 A which is pretty close to the 0.1μ size of the sarcolemma described by the optical microscopists. As Robertson points out we are faced, of course, with the decision as to which of these many structures can be regarded as the true membrane. What we are in fact dealing with here is really a membrane complex rather than a single membrane and this, strictly speaking, applies to the membranes of all other cells as well. Every now and again the sarcolemma is penetrated by holes which are the ends of the caveolae intracellulares. Some of these little openings or caveolae expand into vesicles and in some cases both the vesicles and the caveolae themselves may extend in a complicatd fashion, branching and ramifying over and in between the myofibrils. It has been suggested by Bennett and also by Palade that such caveolae are not a standardized feature of the structure of the sarcolemma of the muscle fiber, in general, but that they represent a mechanism whereby ions or macromolecules such as carbohydrates or proteins can obtain access into the interior of the fibers without violating the osmotic properties of the membrane. There do not appear to be pores in the sarcolemmal membrane so far as present investigations have shown, but Bennett has suggested in his chapter on the fine structure of muscle in the present authors' "Structure and

Function of Muscle," Academic Press, 1960, that various substances (e.g., proteins and carbohydrates) would be bound to the outer surface of the sarcolemma. According to the nature of the binding sites there, the membrane would then infold, form a caveola, and this would seal off to form a vesicle and the vesicle would then pass into the interior and might then be destroyed so that the substances become free in the cytoplasm. This is a pinocytotic type of interpretation of these caveolae and the possibility exists, of course, that this type of activity may occur in many types of cells.

Compounds could be passed out of the muscle fiber in a similar way, that is, by becoming attached to the internal surface of the plasma membrane which would then surround it and open up to form a caveola and the contents would become liberated to the exterior. Thus large macromolecules could get through the membrane without actually piercing it.

It is of interest that in connection with this theory Whatman and Mostyn (1955) noted droplets of fat which had been stained with fat dyes in the process of passing through the sarcolemma of cardiac muscle fibers. Quite a number of cells and perhaps all cells appear to have attached on the outside some sort of polysaccharide coating to the plasma membrane. Such a coating occurs on the surface of mammalian erythrocytes where it is extremely thin, and it has been pointed out that this may represent the surface coating which causes the ABO agglutination reaction.

Plant cells are, of course, expert in putting polysaccharides around the outside of their cell membranes, and bacteria consistently do this too. Outside the sarcolemma there also appears to be a cloud of material, approximately 500 A thick which is possibly polysaccharide material. It is of interest that there is a positive periodic acid–Schiff (PAS) reaction in the sarcolemma and this may be the cause of the reaction. This significance of the polysaccharide complex may be its ability to bind various molecules which

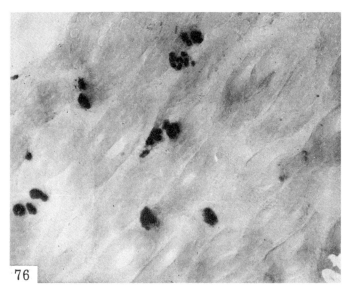

76

FIG. 76. *Cholinesterase in human neuromuscular junctions (motor end-plates). (Preparation and photograph by Dr. Evelyn Beckett.)*

are to be taken into the interior of the muscle membrane.

In the region of the motor end-plates there is considerable modification of the sarcolemma, and Robertson in 1956 and Couteaux in a series of papers have published detailed accounts of this. The sarcolemma in the region of the motor end-plate is very much thicker, denser, and more folded particularly into a series of troughs which penetrate deeply into the sarcoplasm of the muscle fiber. The external polysaccharide-like material just described is present everywhere and separates the actual endings of the neural components of the motor end-plate from the sarcolemmal membrane itself.

The motor end plate as demonstrated by the cholinesterase technique is shown by Fig. 76.

The sarcoplasm of the muscle fiber was originally described by Spidel in 1939 as being in a gelled condition, this can change to a sol if there is any damage to the muscle.

The sarcoplasm not only surrounds the nucleus and is obvious in that part of the fiber (see Fig. 77) but it also penetrates and surrounds and fills in the spaces between the myofibrils themselves and between the myofibrils and sarcolemma. The relative amounts of sarcoplasm in the fibers varies very considerably, and it is of interest that Golarz and Bourne have demonstrated great activity for the enzyme acetyl phosphatase in the sarcoplasm of human muscle. The sarcoplasm also contains most of the soluble proteins of the muscle fiber. Under the electron microscope it is less dense than the other components of the fiber. There are also a number of small granules scattered about the sarcoplasm which show a great range in size, something between ten and a couple of hundred angstroms across. They are distributed without any particular pattern, and in some regions of the sarcoplasm there do not appear to be any at all. They appear to be more abundant in certain areas of the sarcoplasm in heart muscle fibers, and, according to Fawcett and Selby (1958) they may, in fact, be composed of glycogen. Such areas give a strong PAS reaction, and, if the section is treated with amylase prior to application of the PAS reaction, the reaction disappears. This is strong evidence that these granules are, in fact, glycogen.

Beckett and Bourne have demonstrated that PAS positive material was present which was dispersed irregularly in human muscle fibers, sometimes as irregularly distributed aggregates and sometimes as fine granules. To some extent the difference in size of these granules depends on the changes which take place following death. A biopsy specimen, for instance, shows only small granules and aggregations but by 12 hrs. the aggregates have reached their optimum size and after 48 hrs. autolytic procedures have removed them altogether. Beckett and Bourne have demonstrated that the amount of stainable material with the PAS technique in normal muscles is extremely variable and

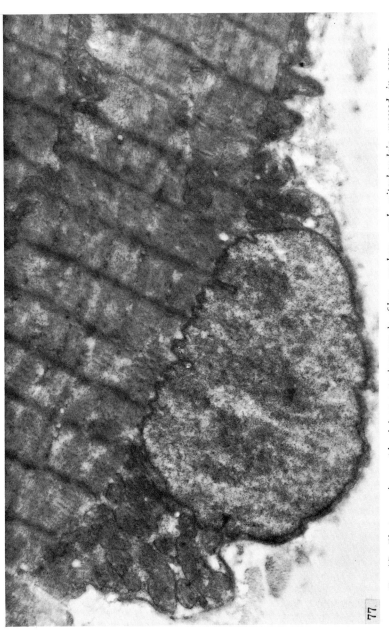

Fig. 77. *Electron micrograph of frog sartorius muscle fiber. nucleus, and mitochondria massed in sarcoplasm. (Preparation and photograph by R. Quinton Cox, Dept. of Anatomy, Emory Univ.)*

77

that there is no correlation between the amount present and the anatomical site of the muscle concerned. Also in muscular and neuromuscular disorders the amount of stainable material is variable and inconstant and shows no particular relationship with the neuromuscular diseases which were studied. For details see the article on this subject in "Structure and Function of Muscle," 1960, Vol. III.

It is of interest that Dempsey and his colleagues and Beckett and Bourne were unable to remove all this PAS positive material with either diastase or saliva. This suggests that we are dealing either with glycogen which is linked to and protected by protein in some way or with a mucopolysaccharide type of substance or possibly even aldehyde groups are being produced by the PAS reaction by lipids or fat. Beckett and Bourne also applied the McManus PAS technique to formalin fixed, frozen sections in conjunction with the Sudan black test for fats. These were made both on rat and human muscle. By this frozen section method it was found that the muscle fiber was stained in a regular diffuse positive PAS background staining and there were also droplets of the material giving a strikingly intense positive PAS reaction. These droplets are often considerably increased in pathological muscles and appear to accumulate at points of mechanical damage in muscle fibers. These strongly positive droplets do not appear to be glycogen. Paraffin embedding of the muscle, however, removes these droplets. It is possible because of these facts that they may be a lipid of some sort. They are not, however, sudanophilic (thus are probably not fat) and do not give a Schultz reaction for cholesterol.

Many muscles fibers contain droplets of fat in the sarcoplasm. These vary very considerably in individual muscle fibers, in individual muscles, and in individual muscles as a whole. Some muscles have more fat than other muscles. This was first described as long ago as 1841 by Henle and subsequently investigated by Kölliker (1846), and others. Fat was recorded in human muscle as long ago as 1889.

Beckett and Bourne using the Sudan black technique in human muscle found that fat could occur in droplets of very variable size, distributed at random, but that a few were situated at the poles of the nuclei. Also there was some staining in the regions of the cross striations with Sudan black.

Some muscle fibers have a red color and some have a white color. Red and white muscles are well known amongst mammals, and in animals such as the rabbit and guinea pig and also in the turkey both red and white muscles occur separately, but generally speaking, particularly in humans, muscles are a mixture of both red and white fibers. The red color of the fiber depends upon the fact that it contains myoglobin or muscle hemoglobin. The red fibers contract more slowly and remain contracted for a longer period than the white muscles. There are more of them in those muscles which are concerned with posture. Generally speaking too, the red muscle fibers contain more sarcoplasm than the white and they also appear to contain more fat which presumably functions as a reserve supply of energy for the muscle fiber.

Ribonucleic acid granules have not been identified in the sarcoplasm of adult muscle. An interesting new development in the structure of muscle fibers is the delineation of the sarcoplasmic reticulum described by Bennett in his chapter on "Structure and Function of Muscle." As Bennett points out, for more than 100 years papers have reported that there appears to be some sort of a network or series of tubules associated with muscle fibers. Retzius in 1881, had described a sarcoplasmic network and Kölliker had referred to a network in 1888, however, the most detailed treatment was given by Veratty in 1902. He described a "reticular apparatus" in muscle, this is a confusing term since the Golgi apparatus had often been referred to in these terms. Bennett and Porter in 1953, found this component in electron-microscope pictures of muscle and described it as a sarcoplasmic reticulum. Sjöstrand and his colleagues subsequently referred to

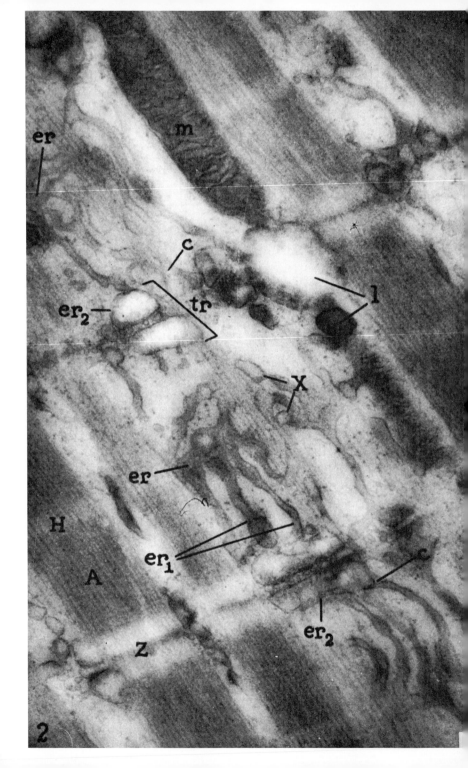

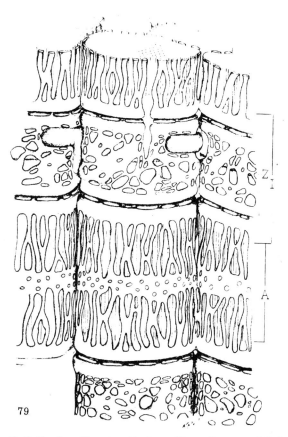

79

FIG. 78 (left). Sarcoplasmic reticulum. (From Porter and Palade, J. Biophys. Biochem. Cytol., 3, 269, 1957.)

FIG. 79 (above). A schematic summary and interpretation of observations on the sarcoplasmic reticulum of rat sartorius muscle. A single myofibril occupies the center of the image with portions of adjacent myofibrils surrounding it. A complete sarcomere with associated reticulum is pictured as part of the central fibril. Sarcosomes, shown in less than the normal number, occupy well defined positions relative to the Z line. They are pictured with their long axes oriented circumferentially with respect to the fibril and covered or not by the close reticulum of the I band region. × approximately 32,000. (Legend and figure from Porter and Palade, J. Biophys. Biochem. Cytol., 3, 269, 1957.)

them as sarcotubules. It is of interest that the work on this reticulum which was described and understood very well by these early workers appeared to be completely ignored in later books of histology where one finds scarcely any reference at all to what now appears to be a very important structure in the muscle fibers.

The work of Bennett and Porter and a number of other investigators has demonstrated that this reticulum really resembles in its fine structure the endoplasmic reticulum found in other cells. Its membranes have the triple structure comparable with what Robertson described as the "unit membrane." These tubules appear to extend inward from the sarcolemma. The work by A. F. Huxley and his colleagues has indicated that there is probably a structure in the muscle fiber which is capable of transmitting depolarization of an ion aligned membrane into the interior of the muscle. These authors, in fact, found that you could get a localized contraction of a muscle fiber by stimulation in certain spots and, if the sarcoplasmic reticulum is, in fact, the component in the fiber which has this function, then presumably these are the spots on the sarcolemma where the sarcoplasmic reticulum or at least one unit of it begins. Porter and Palade made a very detailed study of the sarcoplasmic reticulum with the electron microscope (see Figs. 78 and 79). The reticulum appears to be arranged in the form of alternating sets of tubes which anastomose with each other and surround the fiber like a bracelet. The anastomosing of the tubules gives the general impression of a lacelike type of structure. One set of these tubules has a plane of symmetry at the Z band and extends on each side of it to about the junction between the A and I bands, alternating between these is a series of tubules which is in the plane of the M bands. It should be emphasized that these structures which are being described are characteristic both of skeletal muscle and cardiac muscle.

Characteristic Golgi apparatus is also found in the sarcoplasm of muscle close to the nucleus as one might expect. Although we have referred to a striated muscle fiber as a cell, probably it is really a number of cells since any one striated muscle fiber may contain a number of nuclei and in a very long fiber, which measures several centimeters in length, some hundreds of nuclei may be present. They lie at the surface of the fibers (except in cardiac muscle where they are in the center) just under the sarcolemma surrounded by sarcoplasm. The nuclei are generally oval in shape, with their long axes parallel with the long axis of the fiber, they are approximately $8-10\mu$ long and may be extended as much as 17μ. They are hard to see in unstained fresh muscle fibers but come out very well in fixed and stained preparations. In muscle diseases and in degenerating muscle, they appear to migrate into the center of the fiber and one can see long strings of muscle nuclei aligned end-to-end along the center of the fiber. It is of interest that in embryonic muscle fibers the nuclei occupy a middle rather than a hypolemmal (close to the sarcolemma) position.

The fine structure of muscle nuclei does not differ from those of other cells. The nuclei are surrounded by two unit membranes analogous to the membranes of the endoplasmic reticulum of other cells. In fact, Bennett thought the outer membrane of these pairs may be continuous with the cytomembranes which are found in the perinuclear cytoplasm or even continuous with those of the sarcoplasmic reticulum, in which case the arrangement of the sarcoplasmic structure is fundamentally the same in muscle fibers as in other cells. The membrane of the muscle nucleus also contains a number of pores.

The fibrils of the muscle fibers are the contractile elements. They appear to extend for the entire length of the fiber and they are approximately $1-3\mu$ in diameter. Muscle fibers under the light microscope show a well-defined cross striation (see Fig. 80) and this, of course, is visible in the fibrils, and it is of interest that the individual fibrils are aligned so that the appropriate segments of their bands

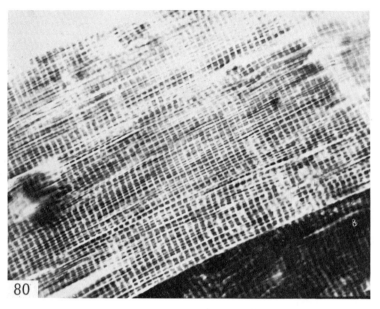

80

FIG. 80. *Cross striations in skeletal muscle fibers of rat. The division of the fibers into longitudinal fibrils can be seen. (Preparation by Dr. Evelyn Beckett; photograph by the present author.)*

FIG. 81. *Electron micrograph of frog sartorius muscle. Note cross striations, sarcosomes, and some black irregular lipid droplets between muscle fibers. (Preparation and Photograph by R. Quinton Cox, Dept. of Anatomy, Emory Univ.)*

coincide with each other. Between the fibrils are the sarcosomes or muscle mitochondria, to which we will return in a little while. (See Fig. 81.)

It is interesting to note that the fibrils consist simply of orientated protein molecules and do not have a surface membrane, therefore the substances in solution in the cytoplasm can have a direct influence on the protein of the fibrils. They have unrestricted access to each other.

The transverse striations of the fibrils of the muscle fiber are due to a difference in density see Fig. 80. These cross striations form a pattern and each pattern repeats along the whole of the length of the fiber and each repeating part of the pattern is known as a "sarcomere." In vertebrate muscle each sarcomere is about $2-3\mu$ in length. The fibril itself is constructed of filaments which are made of protein and which lie parallel to the long axis of the fiber and overlap each other. There are two kinds of these filaments,

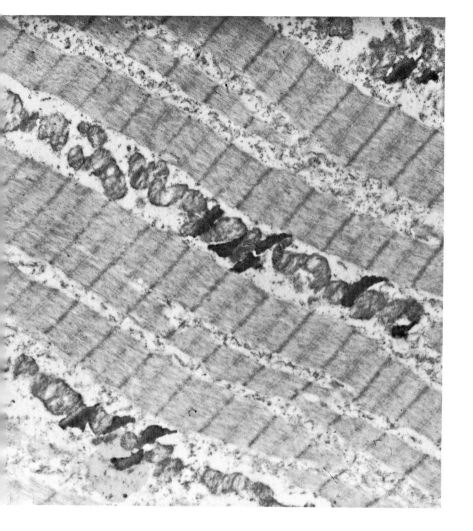

one being about twice the diameter of the other and they are also different in length. These two types alternate along the length of the fibril and they overlap at parts and interdigitate with each other. The regions where the thick filaments are located are known as the "A" bands, these are extremely dense and are anisotropic under the polarizing microscope. Where the thin filaments are present there is less density and there is less birefringence, these are known as the I or isotropic bands. There is a band which appears across the middle of these which is called a Z membrane or band.

At the center of the A or anisotropic band, thick filaments are present alone but at both ends of the A band there is interdigitation of the thin and the thick filaments and this is the densest part of the fibril. The part of the A band where the thick filaments occur alone is called the H band and is naturally not as dense as the rest of the A band. The Z membrane is due to the presence of a band of amorphous material which occupies the spaces between the filaments at the mid-point of the area where the thin filaments are located (the I band). In the case of the A bands, thickening of the thick filaments themselves about the middle of the band causes them apparently to be cut across by what is described as the M line or as the M strip by some authors.

The filaments which compose the fibrils of the muscle fiber are made up of protein and there appear to be three proteins concerned: myosin, actin, and tropomyosin. There is more myosin than any other protein; it constitutes approximately 54% of the total protein of the fibrils. There is only about 11% of tropomysin but about 20–25% of actin. This leaves a deficiency about 10% in total protein, and it is possible, according to Huxley and Hanson in their chapter in the "Structure and Function of Muscle," that the figures for the various proteins are a little too low particularly for tropomyosin and probably for actin too.

It appears that myosin is the protein of the thick filaments which constitute the A bands of the fibers. Actin, on the other hand, appears to be the protein which makes up the thin filaments of the I bands. Tropomyosin also appears to be present where the actin is situated. *In vitro* actin and myosin form a complex called actomyosin and this can be persuaded to contract under the influence of ATP just as the muscle fiber contracts under appropriate stimulation *in vivo*. Each filament of myosin appears to contain 425 molecules. If myosin is treated with trypsin, it splits into two types of meromyosins—one which is called light and the other heavy meromyosin. These meromyosins apparently occur as distinct units in the myosin molecule. Huxley and Hanson suggest that the backbone of a filament of myosin is made up of light meromyosin units which are longitudinally arranged and staggered, and the heavy meromyosin units, which are attached to the light meromyosins and project from the filaments, these projections can be seen under the electron microscope (see Fig. 82).

The number of molecules in each filament of actin can also be calculated and they amount to approximately 600. There is some evidence that the actin filaments contain tropomyosin and, according to Huxley and Hanson, there are about 1.7 molecules of actin to 1 of tropomyosin. The way these two proteins are linked in the filaments is not known.

Huxley and Hanson believe that the actin molecules are exposed at the surface of the filament so that they may form actomyosin links with the neighboring myosin filaments where they interdigitate. The difficult thing to explain is the fact that a muscle can contract very strongly without significant change in the length of its filaments. There are a number of experiments which have been carried out to elucidate this point. However, it appears that what probably happens is that the shortening of the muscle fiber takes place by a sliding of the actin filaments in between the myosin filaments of the A band; they already interdigitate at their ends and the actin filaments simply slide further in (see Fig. 83). In the noncontracting muscle the

FIG. 82. *Electron micrograph of frog sartorius muscle. Note myosin (thick) filaments and actin (thin) filaments interdigitating. Note cross linking between filaments. (Preparation and photograph by R. Quinton Cox, Dept.*

82

little bumps which have been mentioned before (projections on the heavy meromyosin filaments) come in contact with the actin filaments at the regions of interdigitation and these lock to form an actomyosin complex. Now this happens when no ATP is present, but when ATP is present these locks break apart and the actin filaments can slide up into the myosin filaments. When ATP is dephosphorylated then the locks will form again, and it is possible that in contraction the actin filaments slip into the myosin filaments point-by-point, there being a locking and releasing corresponding to the production and dephosphorylation of ATP. Then when all the ATP formed is dephosphorylated the bands lock again. As soon as ATP is re-formed then the locks break and the actin filaments can slide out from the A bands again and the muscle becomes extended. Thus ATP is necessary both for contraction and relaxation of muscle. It is a very interesting fact that the enzyme ATPase which is responsible for the dephosphorylation of ATP is actually the myosin molecule itself. This is a very interest-

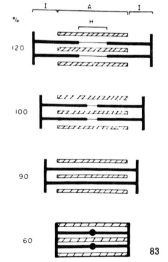

FIG. 83. *Diagram showing H. E. Huxley's view of the molecular basis of contraction of muscle. In this theory shortening of the muscle takes place by the sliding of thick filaments, myosin (black) in between the thin filaments, actin (cross hatched) (From Huxley, Scientific American, November 1958, 67.)*

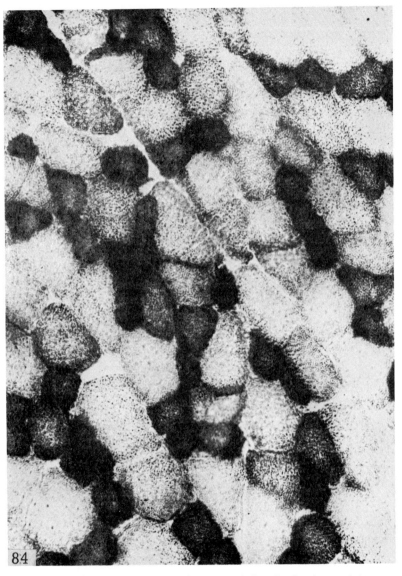

84

Fig. 84 (*above*). *Transverse section of muscle bundle showing succinic dehydrogenase reaction. Note varying* **intensities of reaction in differ-** *ent fibers. (Preparation and photograph by* **Dr.** *Evelyn Beckett.*)

Fig. 85 (*right*). *Flight muscle of insect* Tenebrio. *Note extremely large sarcosomes (mitochondria). These organelles are as big as the muscle fibers. (Preparations by David Smith, photograph by Keith Parker. Permission of Phillips Co., Eindhoven, Netherlands.)*

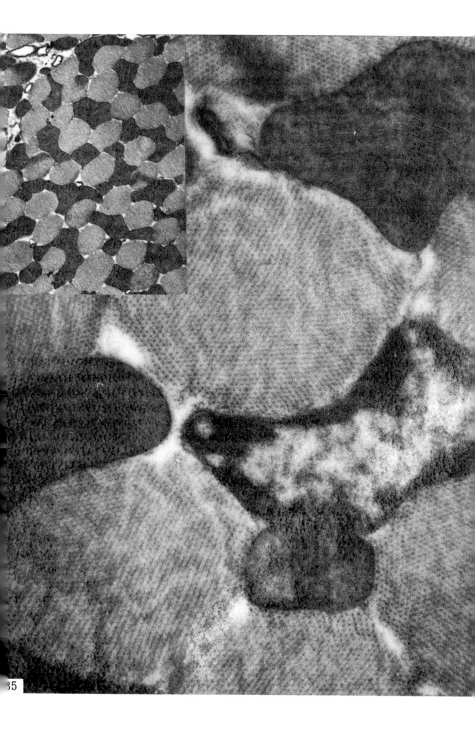

ing example of a structural molecule which is also performing a metabolic function as an enzyme.

One should mention here just briefly one or two of the important chemical reactions which take place in muscle and which play a part in the contraction cycle. We have seen that the sliding of the actin filaments into the myosin filaments is dependent on the periodic formation and dephosphorylation of ATP. The re-formation of ATP is a result of the famous Lohnman reaction: creatine phosphate + ADP = creatine + ATP. The ATP, as has been mentioned before, is a high-energy phosphate and its dephosphorylation results in the liberation of energy which can be used for the mechanical movements necessary by the molecules in the contraction cycle. We do not propose to give full details here of the chemical reactions that take place in muscles in contraction. Anyone interested in this subject can consult the article "Biochemistry of Muscular Action," by Dorothy Needham in "Structure and Function of Muscle," Vol. II.

We might note that the rephosphorylation of ATP requires energy to reconstitute a high-energy bond and this energy can be provided by oxidative phosphorylation produced as a result of coupling respiration with such a process. There are elements in the muscle which are capable of doing this and these elements are the muscle mitochondria, the sarcosomes, which are strategically placed to perform this function. We will say a word now about their structure and position.

The localization (by histochemical means) of succinic dehydrogenase in sarcosomes is shown in Fig. 84.

Electron-microscope studies of the sarcosomes demonstrate that they are identical in their fine structure with that of mitochondria. For example, they have a double membrane, and also internal folds of the inner membrane to form double membrane cristae. They are located in the muscle fibers, at least in the case of heart muscle, exactly opposite the A bands. Slater in his chapter on sarcosomes in "Structure and Function of Muscle" points out that Holmgren had originally classified muscles as falling into two types which depended on the type of distribution of the granules (sarcosomes), and he believed that the two classes corresponded to the two physiological types of muscles. Muscles that had granules at the level of the I bands of the muscle fibrils were those which acted only intermittently, such as the skeletal muscles of most vertebrates, and those which had granules at the level of the A bands were required for continuous activity and in this group would come the flight muscles of birds and insects and, of course, the heart muscles of vertebrates.

It is of interest that, for instance, in the flight muscles of the humming bird and of the hovering insects where there is a phenomenal rate of contraction cycles per second (see Fig. 85), the mitochondria are relatively enormous in comparison with any other structural elements in the fiber, indicating the high rate of oxygen consumption that must be necessary when the fibers are contracting at such high speeds. Also interesting to note is that sarcosomes, like the sarcoplasmic reticulum, were discovered a good many years ago, in the 19th century in fact. Regaud in 1909 had claimed that they were, indeed, identical with mitochondria because they showed similar staining reactions. Yet, in histology books published since then and up to recent times, sarcosomes have been largely ignored in accounts of the histological structure of muscle. Thus, there are two curious facts about the history of muscle structure—the sarcoplasmic reticulum and the sarcosomes were both discovered more than half a century ago and then dropped out completely from the histological picture and from the textbooks.

Not only do the sarcosomes resemble the mitochondria of other cells in staining reactions and in their fine structure, but they also contain the same series of respiratory enzymes, i.e., those enzymes concerned with the Krebs cycle and cytochrome system found in mitochondria. It is of interest that in red muscle fibers, where, as had been mentioned the red color is due to myoglobin, there are more mitochondria than in white fibers and that the myoglobin assists in the rapid transfer of oxygen from the blood to the respiratory enzymes found in the mitochondria.

The chemical reactions which take place in muscle can be stated as follows:

$$C_6H_{12}O_6 + 2 \text{ DPN}^+ + 2 \text{ ADP} + 2 \text{ P (inorganic)} \rightarrow$$
$$2 \text{ CH}_3 \cdot \text{CO} \cdot \text{COOH} + 2 \text{ DPNH} + 2 \text{ H} + 2 \text{ ATP} \qquad \text{(I)}$$

$$2 \text{ CH}_3 \cdot \text{CO} \cdot \text{COOH} + 5 \text{ O}_2 + 30 \text{ ADP} + 30 \text{ P (inorganic)} \rightarrow$$
$$6 \text{ CO}_2 + 4 \text{ H}_2\text{O} + 30 \text{ ATP} \qquad \text{(II)}$$

$$2 \text{ DPNH} + 2 \text{ H}^+ + \text{O}_2 + 6 \text{ ADP} + 6 \text{ P (inorganic)} \rightarrow$$
$$2 \text{ DPN}^+ + 2 \text{ H}_2\text{O} + 6 \text{ ATP} \qquad \text{(III)}$$

Reaction I appears to be restricted to the sarcoplasm, in non-muscle cells it is in the cytoplasm; reactions II and III take place in the sarcosomes as they do in the mitochondria. If we sum up those three reactions,

$$C_6H_{12}O_6 + 6 \text{ O}_2 + 38 \text{ ADP} + 38 \text{ P (inorganic)} \rightarrow$$
$$6 \text{ CO}_2 + 6 \text{ H}_2\text{O} + 38 \text{ ATP}$$

we see that the sum of the activities of these processes in the muscle is the synthesis of 38 molecules of ATP for each time the cycle occurs. The function of the sarcosomes in the muscle fibers appears to be the provision of ATP for the functioning of the contractile elements. The myofibrils have no membrane, the sarcosomes are virtually in contact with the myofibrils, and the ATP can diffuse almost instantaneously into the sarcofibrillar filament. If an inadequate supply of oxygen is available or in muscles with an insufficient amount of sarcosomes, the DPNH and the pyruvic acid which are formed as a result of reaction I produce lactic acid. This reaction is

$$\text{CH}_3 \cdot \text{CO} \cdot \text{COOH} + \text{DPNH} + \text{H}^+ \rightarrow \text{CH}_3\text{CHOH} \cdot \text{COOH} + \text{DPN}^+$$

It is also of interest that sarcosomes can bring about oxidation of fatty acids, and in the oxidation of stearic acid as much as 147 molecules of ATP are formed with each reaction. Also sarcosomes, similarly to mitochondria and other cell organelles, may become unstable if ATP is not present, and, according to Slater, this suggests that some energy provided by the ATP is necessary to stabilize the structure of these organelles. It is believed that ATP is also used to some extent to maintain a difference in the concentration of ions as between the sarcosomes and the rest of the cytoplasm. Here then, in the muscle fiber we have probably a division of labor as well defined as one could find in any cell in the body. There is a special part of the cell, the contractile part, which is exclusively used for this purpose, not only that but we have the contractile protein acting as an enzyme which can trigger off the whole process. The ATP which is necessary for the process is provided by the oxidative phosphorylations coupled with the respiration of the mitochondria which are themselves in close physical contact with the fibrils. The changes in ionic polarization of the membranes which are initiated by the motor endplate and which pass along the sarcolemma can be carried into the fibrils of the muscle fiber by means of the sarcoplasmic endoreticulum. Furthermore, the sarcolemma appears to be adapted to undergo pinocytosis and can take macromolecules directly into the sarcoplasm. This is, the perfect example of division of labor in cells and yet it should be pointed out again how much these individual labors depend on and are integrated with each other.

THE NERVE FIBER

In conclusion, we will consider the nerve cell and the nerve fiber. The nerve fiber itself is not a cell but it is a prolongation of a cell. It is a process of a neuron which is adapted for carrying nervous impulses. The functioning of the nerve fiber is a little more mysterious at the moment than is, for instance, the muscle fiber since we have little in the way of moving parts to investigate and a great deal of the information which is available is theoretical. Most of the studies on the physiology of the nerve fiber are devoted to the movements of ions, particularly sodium and potassium ions, in and out of the nerve fiber membrane since it is believed that it is the polarization and depolarization of the membrane produced by these ions which constitutes the passage of a nerve impulse along the fiber. The nerve fiber originates from the neuron, from a conical area known as the cone of origin. The nerve cell itself contains a well-defined nucleus and nucleolus. There are numerous Nissl bodies.

Among the characteristic structures classically described in the nerve cell are (1) neurofibrils, (2) Nissl bodies also called tigroid bodies because of their striped appearance which suggested a resemblance to the coat of a tiger to earlier investigators, (3) Golgi apparatus, (4) mitochondria, (5) fats, phospholipids, and (6) pigments.

Neurofibrils have been claimed to be present in all nerve cells and in the axon, but there is some doubt as to whether they exist as structural elements in the living cells although up to the beginning of the century they had been regarded as the basis of nerve impulse propagation. There is evidence from microdissection that in the living nerve cells of invertebrates they exist as discrete threadlike structures which are interwoven with each other and appear to be more viscous than the surrounding neuroplasm. In fixed and stained preparations, the neurofibrils are extremely fine and it is not surprising therefore they are hard to see in the living cell. Fibrous structures have, however, been seen in the cytoplasm of nerve cells in tissue cultures and, if fresh nervous tissue is treated with salts such as $CaCl_2$ or various fixatives, the neurofibrils rapidly come into view. One view is that the neurofibril is a rodlet sol, that it is composed of orientated molecular particles which are not, in fact, sufficiently strongly attached to each other to form a definite fibril, but that a variety of agents may cause these rodlets to precipitate as fibrils.

Electron-microscope preparations also show Nissl bodies in nerve cells. They may be stained by basic aniline dyes, and in specially fixed nervous material, histochemical tests have shown that they contain phosphoric acid and iron and they also appear to contain ribonucleic acid. In certain acute pathological conditions the Nissl bodies may disappear. This is a process known as chromatolysis and, if there is injury to the axon, the appropriate nerve cells show central chromatolysis, that is, the dissolution of the Nissl bodies surrounding the nucleus. There is also a loss of Nissl material from the central neurones of birds in long transmigratory flights. Under ultraviolet light Nissl bodies have the appearance of a flocculant precipitate, and it has been shown that they can be displaced in the cell prior to fixation by ultracentrifugation.

Classic Golgi preparations show that the Golgi apparatus exists as a network close to and wholly or partly surrounding the nucleus, in fact, it was in nerve cells, as we have stated earlier, that Golgi first discovered the apparatus which is called after him.

Mitochondria are fairly obvious in properly stained nerve cells and in cell bodies they tend to be spherical but in the dendrites they are more elongated while in the axon they may appear as long filaments. Near the nucleus there may be an accumulation of fatty-like droplets which may be Golgi material and in a similar position two types of pigment may also be found, e.g., in the *substantia migra* of the midbrain a black-to-red melanin pigment occurs in this site in the cell. Many neurons show the presence of yellow droplets of lipochrome pigment. The cell membrane of the nerve cells is an extremely delicate structure much finer than the nuclear membrane. Electron microscopy demonstrates that it cannot be more than a few hundredths of a micron thick, whereas the nuclear membrane is about $1/10\mu$ thick, probably due to its nature as a double fold of the endoplasmic reticulum. There is some evidence from the electron microscope that the cytoplasm of nerve cells is of high water content and that the material of the axon is still more dilute. The axon itself arises from an elevated portion

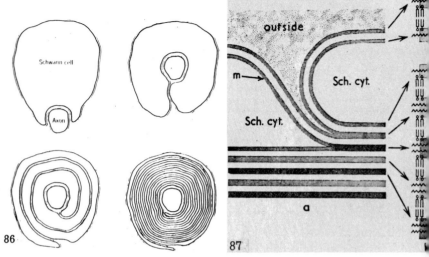

FIG. 86 (*left*). *Schematic representation of the membrane theory of the origin of nerve myelin, (after Geren). Four stages in the engulfment of the axon by the Schwann cell and the wrapping of many double layers which, after condensation, form the compact myelin. (Figure and legend from Schmitt, Reviews of Modern Physics, 31, 455, 1959.)*

FIG. 87 (*right*). *This diagram illustrates the relationships of the enfolded Schwann cell membrane in a mesaxon (or meso) of an adult myelinated fiber. The two cell membranes come together along their outside surfaces to form the outermost myelin lamella. The inside surfaces of the mesaxon loops are in apposition at the major dense lines in compact myelin. Three complete repeating units of myelin are indicated in (a). The molecular structure of the outer two repeating lamellae is indicated in (b). At the top the molecular structure of the Schwann cell membrane is indicated. The molecular diagrams are based on Finean's model. The stippling superimposed on the molecular model indicates the densities which are observed after permanganate fixation. (Figure and legend from Schmitt, Review of Modern Physics, 31, 455, 1959.)*

of the neuron called the axon hillock or cone of origin and it may give off branches or collaterals but it usually ends in arborizations known as telodendria. A short way from the cell body, the axon develops a number of sheaths and becomes a nerve fiber. If it has a well-defined myelin sheath, it is known as a myelinated nerve. (For the suggested embryological origin of this sheath see Fig. 86) and if not, as an unmyelinated nerve fiber. Studies with polarized light however and with the electron microscope lead us to believe that all nerve fibers possess some type of lipoprotein sheath similar to the myelin sheath. Studies of the myelin sheath using polarized light, x-ray diffraction, and later electron microscopy (particularly in the last case the work of Fernandez-Moran should be mentioned) have shown that lipoid and protein are laid down essentially in a series of alternating concentric layers. These lipoprotein layers appear to be about 130 A thick and the protein sections to be about 30 A thick. The lipid and the protein molecules of which these layers are composed are oriented radially, that is at right angles to the surface of the fiber. (See Fig. 87.)

When hematoxylin and eosin preparations are made of nerves fixed by conventional fixatives in the usual way and embedded in wax, a reticulate structure can be seen in the myelin sheaths which is known as the neurokeratin network. We shall have more to say about this later. Every now and again the myelin sheath becomes divided at the node of Ranvier, the neurilemmal sheath is continuous at this point but the myelin sheath itself is interrupted. The reason for this is not known but it is possible that the myelin may be a type of liquid crystal. This would probably be unstable in a tube longer than that represented by the internodes between the two adjacent nodes of Ranvier. It has been mentioned that the axon is also in a semifluid condition and, under the polarizing microscope, it can be seen to be birefringent suggesting a regular molecular orientation which is not incompatible with fluidity since it represents another form of liquid crystal similar to that of the myelin sheath but its chemical composition is different from that of the latter.

It has been found that the concentraton of ions is different inside and outside the cell and the nerve fiber; sodium and chloride, for instance, have a higher concentration extracellularly and potassium intracellularly. An electrical potential exists across the cell membrane because of this difference. Both sodium and potassium diffuse across cell membranes so that presumably they would eventually become equally distributed on either side of the membrane and the membrane potential would then disappear. But this does not happen, and a factor which prevents it is a metabolic "pump" which maintains the difference in ion distribution. The level of the membrane potential depends upon the ratio of (K^+) and (Cl^-) ions and the rate at which the sodium ion (Na^+) is pumped.

The presence of a membrane potential along a nerve membrane is essential for the passage of an impulse. In the resting condition the membrane is known as the K^+ membrane. During the passage of an impulse the potential across the nerve membrane changes, this is known as the action potential, and is due to a change in the permeability of the membrane and a sudden influx of sodium ions. The nerve fiber membrane is then called a (Na^+) membrane. The recovery of the membrane and the reestablishment of a (K^+) membrane starts with an increase in permeability to (K^+) ions and a decrease in permeability to (Na^+) ions. These changes finally bring the potential back to the resting value.

The studies on the conductance of (Na^+) and (K^+) ions in nerve were carried out by Hodgkin and Katz with the introduction of the membrane voltage clamping technique. In effect what they demonstrated was that the movement of (Na^+) into the fiber during the passage of an impulse depolarizes the membrane by carrying electrical charges through it. The reestablishment of a resting potential across the fibers (the K membrane) requires the sodium ions to be pumped out against a gradient of (Na^+). This can only be done by the use of energy. That metabolic processes are involved in this action is indicated by the relatively high oxygen uptake of nerve.

By using optical methods, it has also been demonstrated

that changes in the electrical activity of the nerve fiber which are associated with the passage of a stimulus are associated with changes in the optical density or in the light scattering capacity of the fiber. The scattering of light by the fiber indicates change of volume. It is of interest that this swelling is maintained for several seconds after the summated action of several series of impulses. The rate of change in optical density is not comparable to the velocity of propagation of the action potential, but there appears to be a connection between the wave of excitation and the optical changes. However, the nature of this connection is obscure at the moment.

The fluid substance of the axon is believed to be under pressure. As evidence for this one might quote the experiments of Paul Weiss in Chicago, who found that if a nerve fiber is ligated, the axoplasm is dammed up to the point where the constriction occurs and when pressure is released it flows forward again. He also showed that, if a nerve fiber is cut, the axonal material will stream out from the cut surface. It has also been shown that, if such a severed nerve is stimulated, the speed of outflow of axoplasm is decreased. This appears to be due to gelatinization of the axoplasm and a consequent increase in its viscosity.

In our laboratory at Emory University Professor Portela and his colleagues have been making studies of the correlation of physicochemical properties of the axoplasm in a state of excitation. Studies are being made with an interference microscope of surface movements of the nerve in response to "stimulation" and these movements are being recorded simultaneously with change in action potential. The surface movements of the nerve are indicated by the reflection of interference fringes in the interference microscope of the light from the nerve surface.

It is interesting to note that the Russian authors Kayushin and Lyudkovskaya believed that the surface movements (as expressed by shifts in the interference bands) result from changes in the fiber volume and since these shifts disappeared when there was no stimulation, it appeared that these volume changes had returned to normal and the movement was probably of an elastic nature. These mechanical waves (surface movements, volume changes) are presumably connected with changes of the molecular micellar structure in the nerve. Thus, it appears that the whole of the structural system of the nerve takes part in the conduction of an impulse. This way of looking at the relationship between molecular structure and the excitation-conduction-recovery cycle in the nerve is a new approach to the investigation of nerve physiology.

It is possible that the mechanical waves in the nerve fiber push acetylcholine down toward the myoneural junction, and there is some evidence this compound may be formed either in the axon or possibly in the cell body itself. There is evidence of considerable synthesis of protein by nerve cells but the significance of this is not known.

In our laboratory attempts are being made to correlate the lipid and protein structure and organization of the nerve and function of the nerve as a conductor. The approach is similar to that of Tobias. Proteolytic and lipolytic enzymes are used to produce structural changes in the nerve fiber and afterward records of interference and electrical measurements and fine structural changes are made. The removal of phospholipids from the nerve membrane results in the nerve becoming inexcitable but, following treatment with proteolytic enzymes, nerve conduction is not blocked.

It is of interest that pressure (about 1½ lbs.) on the nerve will cause an interruption of the normal function of a motor but not of a sensory nerve and this may last some two weeks before coming completely back to normal. This is particularly curious when such pressure produces no microscopically visible degenerative changes in the nerve fiber.

The cell membrane in nerve fibers is complicated because of the close association of the axon with the Schwann cell. The Schwann cell is associated with the axon in both mye-

linated and nonmyelinated fibers. In the case of the nonmyelinated fibers, the axon is embedded to varying degrees
into the protoplasm of the Schwann cell, but is still surrounded closely by the cell membrane of the Schwann cell
which it has invaginated with it. The actual distance
between the outer parts of the two membranes under these
circumstances is approximately 150 A. The membrane of
the axon and the membrane of the Schwann cell are each
approximately 75 A and are made up of three parts. There
are two rather dense areas which are about 25 A across,
and these are separated from each other by a less dense
area also about 25 A across. So that we may consider that
the membrane of the nerve fiber is enlarged to this extent
by the membrane of the Schwann cell itself.

In myelinated fibers the axon instead of just being embedded in the cytoplasm of the Schwann cell is surrounded
by many layers of Schwann cell cytoplasm and cell membrane. The mechanism which produces this has been demonstrated by Geren in tissue cultures of developing nerve
fibers. She demonstrated that the Schwann cell winds in a
spiral fashion around the axon thus building up many layers
of Schwann cell membrane around the axon itself. Many
degrees of myelination of nerve fibers are known, and the
degree of myelination depends on the number of times the
Schwann cell winds around the axon.

Electron-microscope studies of myelinated nerve fibers
have demonstrated very complex arrangements of the myelin so produced. The first of the high-resolution studies of
such fibers were produced by Fernandez-Moran and Sjö-
strand. If a myelinated nerve is first fixed in osmium
tetroxide (osmic acid), it could be seen that the myelin was
made up of a series of lines which absorbed the osmium
very strongly. These lines were approximately 25 A thick
and repeated at a period of up to 120 A. Each of these
dark lines was separated by a light line of approximately
the same size, and running across the center of each light
line was a line which was more dense than the light line

but less dense than the main 25-A repeating lines. In interpreting the significance of these lines, Robertson has pointed out that the gap, which in the unmyelinated fibers was between the two cell membranes and measured 75 A across, is largely eliminated in myelinated fibers and the outer part of the membrane of the Schwann cell comes into direct contact with the membrane of the axon. Thus we can say that, as Robertson points out, each of the repeating units which are obvious in electron micrographs of the myelin sheath is two Schwann cell membranes in contact along their outside surfaces. The Schwann cell membrane probably consists of a single bimolecular leaflet of lipids of which the hydrophilic ends are associated with monolayers of a nonlipid material and which is probably protein, although there is a possibility that either some polysaccharide or glycoprotein of some sort may be associated with it, possibly on the side directed toward the cytoplasm.

It has recently been shown by Tewari and present author that, in addition to the complex structure demonstrated by the electron microscope, the neurokeratin network previously considered to be a fixation artifact of myelin may indicate the presence of some differentiation of the myelin sheath in the living nerve fiber and the presence of various enzymes including a large variety of phosphatases as well as ATPase and creatine phosphatase (acid phosphatase is restricted to the axon). There is also a good deal of phospholipid as demonstrated by the Baker phospholipid technique. This network has been found, in fact, from these preparations to consist of areas resistant to damage by fixatives and other reagents and apparently arranged in the form of hexagonal prisms which radiate from the axon to the surface of the fiber (actually to the neurilemma) and that it is along these areas that the enzymes and the phospholipid we have mentioned appear to be concentrated. The areas appear to contain at least unsaturated fat and lipid, and it is of interest that, in nerve which has been osmicated for 5 days and extracted with turpentine, it is the material from the interior of these active areas that is extracted, whereas the similarly osmicated material on the faces of the active areas remains. It is possible that the reason why it is retained in the faces of the prisms is due to the fact that the osmicated lipids are bound strongly to a protein and cannot be extracted by turpentine. There is also some evidence that it is held in place by polysaccharide. It is of interest, too, that in these same areas techniques which would normally demonstrate mitochondria and which are presumably really demonstrating a variety of lipoprotein show a localization of similar compounds in the neurokeratin network. It is difficult to reconcile this work with that of electron microscopy. Although if we assume that the protein of the myelin lamellae is enzyme protein in the regions of the neurokeratin network but not in between them, then we can reconcile the two suggested types of structure. We also have to ask what happens to the mitochondria of the Schwann cell when they wrap around the axon. Do they disintegrate or

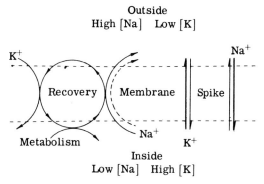

FIG. 88. *Diagrammatic illustration of ion movements through the nerve membrane (after A. L. Hodgkin and R. D. Keynes, J. Physiol. 128, 28, 1955). Ion movements occurring during the action wave are shown at the right; active transport, involving coupling of metabolic energy, is shown on the left. The excitable membrane pictured is presumably identical with the limiting surface membrane of the axon, or some portion thereof. (Figure and legend from Schmitt, Review of Modern Physics, 31, 455, 1959.)*

do they become enormously elongated so that their membranes constitute some of the lamellae described by the electron microscopists.

We have mentioned that there is a high concentration of potassium ions inside the nerve fiber in the axon and much less concentration of sodium. Now it appears that sodium continuously diffuses into the nerve fiber and it must be excreted from the axon to the exterior again. The difficulty about this is that the sodium has to be excreted against a gradient, that is to say, sodium has to be passed out of the axon into a medium where there are more sodium ions than there were in the axon and vice versa with potassium (see Fig. 88). This process requires energy and there have been two principal views as to how this could be done. The two theories are the redox pump and the sodium pump theory.

Conway has suggested the following way in which the outward movement of sodium ions in the nerve fiber could be explained. Sodium ions could be continuously passed on from unsaturated phospholipid molecules to the next unsaturated phospholipid molecules through the membrane to the outside, and there would be alternate oxidation and reduction of the phospholipid molecules as this happened. The other view is that sodium is pumped out by energy produced by presence of ATP, creatine phosphate, and oxidative enzymes and possibly also with the aid of phospholipid. What is not certain yet is whether Na and K ions need to be passed through the myelin sheath to maintain the physiological functioning of the nerve fiber. This is a problem for which we will no doubt get the answer in due course.

It is difficult to draw many conclusions about the division of labor in the nerve fiber. First of all, in the nerve cell we have great production of protein and possibly the production of acetyl choline and the passage of one or both these compounds down the axon toward the myoneural junction; the passage of the nerve impulse is provided for by the axon membrane itself. In myelinated nerves we may have the metabolic mechanism of the neurokeratin network which might be used for pumping ions away from the area of the axon membrane. However, the precise relationship of the myelin sheath to the propagation of the nerve impulse is not known. In myelinated nerves, the impulse appears to be faster than in nonmyelinated or poorly myelinated nerves, and yet one does not know quite in what way the myelin sheath is able to do this. At the termination of the nerve fiber there is a modification in the form of a complex branching in association with the sarcolemma to build up the myoneural junction. There is an accumulation here of acetyl choline which presumably passes through the membrane of the neural part of the mechanism to stimulate the formation of a contraction wave by its influence on the sarcolemmal membrane. The presence of cholinesterase in these junctions, which is necessary for inactivation of acetyl choline after it has done its job, is of interest but its precise origin is unknown. So we can see evidence of division of labor in the nerve cell and its axon but the nature of the labor performed by each part is still partly speculative.

CHAPTER VIII

Conclusion

WE HAVE STUDIED THE structure and to some extent the chemical composition and the biochemical composition of the cell in general and of three specialized types of cells. We have demonstrated that various parts of the cell perform very important but different functions, that, in other words, there is a division of labor. Each part performs the job for which it is chemically and structurally suited; thus the nucleolus synthesizes a considerable amount of protein and ribonucleic acid. We know that the chromosomes of the nucleus contain the genes which produce hereditary effects in the cell. We have seen that the oxidative activities of the cell are carried on in the mitochondria and that, as a result of respiratory activity of these structures, ATP is produced which is available for energy and structural purposes in the cell. In the glandular cell, the ATP provides energy for the synthesis of the products of secretion. In the muscle fiber, it provides the energy for muscular contraction; and presumably in the nerve fiber the myelin sheath provides the energy for the extrusion of Na ions to the neurilemma (although in this latter case this is an example of division of labor between cells. The cytoplasmic (endoplasmic) reticulum is still a very debatable structure; the presence of ribonucleoprotein granules attached to the outside of these membranes indicates that they are probably regions of protein synthesis. If, as is believed by some authors, the cisternae in the endoplasmic reticulum are continuous with the outside we have, in fact, an enormous increase of area of the membrane of the cell. We have the outside world actually penetrating deep into the cytoplasm and even surrounding the nucleus so that nuclear products could be secreted directly to the exterior of the cell without actually passing through the cytoplasm itself. In this way glucose could pass directly into the nucleus as well as directly into the interior of the cytoplasm.

What is so striking in the cytoplasm is not that there is a division of labor but, what is more fantastic, the degree to which all the various parts of the cell cooperate with each other to build up a metabolic picture which is ordered and controlled. This co-operation rarely gets out of gear and when it does disorders of growth and metabolism occur of which one variety can be cancer. The mechanism of cell function is under control of the endocrine system, and we have mentioned earlier in this book how the fine structure of the prostate cell is under control of the male sex hormone and how the localization of acid phosphatase in the same cells is also under control of the same hormone. This is a field which is still scarcely touched and is likely to produce in the future an enormous amount of interesting and valuable information about the function of the cell.

The relationship of vitamins and nutritive factors in general to cell structure is also only beginning to be investigated. Studies on starvation have demonstrated a great increase in the number of mitochondria, and our own studies on scurvy have demonstrated the more intimate association of the endoplasmic reticulum with the mitochondria with a simultaneous increase in the number of mitochondria. Here is a vast field in nutrition where electron microscopy would probably produce immense contributions to a study not only of the physiology of the cell but of the function of vitamins and other nutrients in cell metabolism.

The precarious nature of the cell structure is demonstrated by the fact that the structural integrity of mitochondria is affected in the absence of ATP, and it seems possible that this whole complicated system of energy production is essential not only to provide for cell activity but also energy to maintain the structural integrity of the cell and its organelles; if this is so, then any serious interference with the ATP production cycle will lead to a breakdown of the complex cellular structure as well as interference with the metabolism.

New techniques of cytological investigation have in the last few years made fundamental alterations in our outlook on cell structure and function, and we can expect that the next few years will shed much more light on the intriguing subject of the division of labor in cells.

Subject Index

DATE DUE